Clever Trevor

**Brough Girling
and Tony Blundell**

THE HERO

Young Lions

First published in Great Britain by A & C Black (Publishers) Ltd 1991
First published in Young Lions 1991
Third impression July 1992

Young Lions is an imprint of the Children's Division,
part of HarperCollins Publishers Ltd,
77–85 Fulham Palace Road, Hammersmith, London W6 8JB

Text copyright © 1991 Brough Girling
Illustrations copyright © 1991 Tony Blundell

Printed and bound in Great Britain by
HarperCollins Manufacturing, Glasgow

Samantha lives on this side of the street, at number 40.

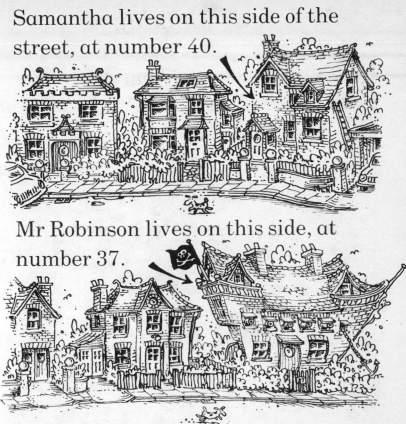

Mr Robinson lives on this side, at number 37.

Samantha is about your age, but a bit better behaved.

This is mostly her story.

Last Monday

Once upon a not very long time ago, Mr Robinson came out of his house and crossed the road.

Soon there was a 'tap tap' at my front door.

I wondered what all this had to do
with me. Like you, I'm an ordinary
sort of person, and not used to
unusual things happening on
Monday mornings.

'What all this has to do with you,'
Mr Robinson went on, 'is that my
mother has asked me not to bring
my parrot with me. She says he
makes her feel a bit ill.'

OK, come on Monday, but don't
you dare bring that parrot
with you. It makes me sick!

Then I noticed a small green parrot
standing on Mr Robinson's shoulder.
I hadn't spotted it before – probably
because I'd been too busy staring at
Mr Robinson's
ear-ring,

and his three-cornered hat with
ostrich feather,

and the fact that he only had one leg.
(Well, he had two, but one of them
wasn't one he'd been born with.)

The parrot was giving me a funny
look.

'He's very well behaved and easy to
look after. I'm sure he'll be no
trouble at all,' said Mr Robinson.

I wasn't really listening, because
Mr Robinson had taken off his hat.
On the top of his head I could see a
tattoo, which read:

Wanted on
voyage.
This side up.

The parrot hopped onto my shoulder
and made sweet little noises
in my ear.

All right

'Much obliged,' said Mr Robinson,
putting back his hat. He turned
smartly, crossed the road and
disappeared into his house to pack.

I went upstairs to my bedroom, with the parrot perched on my shoulder. Gently I stood him on my finger and then coaxed him onto the back of my chair.

He was really tame and stood there with his head tipped to one side. I smiled at him – it's difficult for a parrot to smile back,

because its lips are rather like two sharp pieces of yellow plastic.

In my gentlest, kindest little
voice, I said: 'Who's a pretty boy,
then?'

I just
didn't know
what to say.

'Hey,' I said. 'Parrots are supposed to copy what people say. You aren't meant to answer back.'

'I know that,' squawked the parrot, 'but why do people keep asking me such dumb questions? You can *see* that I'm a pretty boy then, can't you?'

I was amazed.

'Trevor,' said the parrot.
'CLEVER TREVOR!!'

I just stared at the parrot. My
flabber was gasted!
I asked him what he liked to eat.

'Don't you know what a parrot's favourite food is? It's *polyfilla*, of course. I thought everyone knew that one' and he gave a terrible rough laugh.

HA-HA-HA-HA-HA-HA-HA-HA-HA-HA-HA

I realised that there was a lot more to Mr Robinson's parrot than met the eye. I'd thought it was a quiet little bird, but now it looked as if it was going to be like having a rugby team to stay.

Oh well.

Tuesday Morning

When I woke up, Trevor was standing on my bedside table. He followed me around while I got ready for school.

'What are we going to do today, then?' he squawked in my ear, when I was *trying* to clean my teeth. I told him we were going to school because I wanted to show him to Miss Jenkins, our teacher.

'Oh good,' he yelled, 'I think teachers are great. It's because they're in a class of their own!'

-HA-HA-HA-HA-HA-HA-HA-HA-HA-HA-HA-HA-HA-HA

He carried on right up until I set out for school, with him perched on my shoulder. A-HA-HA-HA-HA-HA-HA-HA-HA-HA-HA-HA-HA-HA-HA!!

Meanwhile, in Blackpool, Mr Robinson was having a hard time.

Mind you wipe your foot.

Don't forget to wash behind your ear-ring

Eat up your greens, my lad, or you'll get the scurvy.

Yes, Mum···

···I wish I was back home with Trevor.

Trouble with the School Secretary

At school, I swopped Trevor from the shoulder of my coat to my school jumper. Everybody crowded round and wanted to stroke his feathers.

I thought I was going to be star of the school.

It wasn't until I walked down the corridor past the school secretary's office, that the trouble began . . .

Trouble at Registration

It wasn't a lot better at registration: in fact it was a lot worse. Mrs Jenkins is my favourite teacher. She is kind and friendly, and you can't ever imagine her saying a rude word – even at home if she trips over the cat or opens her bank statement.

Then I showed her Trevor.

Oh, isn't he delightful. Who's a pretty boy, then?

Trouble at Assembly

After registration we all trooped into assembly. Mr Reece said 'Good morning children.' And we all said,

But I could tell that Trevor wasn't paying attention. He had his back to me and was telling jokes to Kevin and Rohana.

Why was the cross-eyed teacher no good at his job?

He couldn't control his pupils!

Things didn't get any better when the vicar started a short prayer to thank Jesus for another nice day.

Then Mr Reece told us that a policeman was going to talk to the infants about Road Safety.

Then it got worse.

What would I be if I joined the army? A *Parrot-trouper!*

And worse.

What's orange and sounds like a parrot? *A carrot!*

I watched as the smiles turned into sniggers, and the grins into giggles.

Soon the whole school was trying
not to laugh. Sally and Jason were
doubled up, clutching their
tummies, and Tariq had to stuff his
hanky in his mouth. The others
were turning purple or red or
magenta.

One or two of the infants wet
themselves, and I think
some of the teachers
nearly did.

Ho Ho!

Ha Ha Ha!

Ha Ha!

Big Trouble with the Head Teacher

It wasn't exactly long before Mr Reece could stand it no longer.

'Stop that laughter!' he said loudly.

OK, WHICH WAY DID IT GO?!

Mr Reece looked like thunder.

'Who is the owner of this terrible
bird?' he growled.

Everything went quiet.

I put my hand up.
Mr Reece looked at me
hard. I tried to explain
about Mr Robinson, and
his mum, and Blackpool.

'If there's any more trouble,' said
Mr Reece, 'you'll hear from me.'

There was a lot more trouble.

In playtime, Trevor went swooping into the boys' toilets and pulled all the toilet paper off its rolls.

None of us knew how he got into one
of the big cupboards in the school
kitchen. But he gave one of the
dinner ladies a horrible fright . . .

An angry dinner lady is one of the
most dangerous animals on earth.
Mrs Higginthorpe picked up a
rolling pin and took off after Trevor,
roaring with rage.

HH!!

But she
couldn't
catch him.

Trevor may be clever,
but he didn't seem
to know that
custard doesn't
go with stew.

Or that sitting
in your food
isn't OK.

Specially if a teacher is watching you.

We were all watching Trevor's terrible tricks. So none of us noticed that two other creatures with not very good table manners were creeping up the drive. And that they were looking for a way to get into school – without using the front door.

Tuesday Afternoon

By the start of afternoon school, there was quite a long list of things that Trevor shouldn't have done:

① Bitten the school secretary.
② Told jokes in assembly.
③ Answered back when spoken to.
④ Wasted toilet paper.
⑤ Frightened Mrs. Higginthorpe.
⑥ Added custard to school stew.

By the end of school, the list was even longer.

Trevor shouldn't have interrupted the netball match. It was totally **wrong of him to swoop down and head the ball away from the basket, just when Sandra Jones was about to score.**

Foul!

I know I'm a fowl!!

Not this one, idiot.

He certainly shouldn't have gone
fishing – especially not in the
tropical fish tank. It's Mr Reece's
pride and joy.

And he shouldn't have
taken a felt-tip
pen and added
to the notice
on the fish tank.

ANTS EGGS

OUR
TROPICAL
FISH.
+ Chips

When our caretaker, Mr Franks, went up a ladder to paint the gutters, Trevor shouldn't have bitten through his braces. And when Mr Franks' trousers fell down, it was very rude of Trevor to laugh, and even worse of him to tell all the infants' mothers to come and look.

He should not have high-dived into the water jugs when we were doing art. (But Mrs Jenkins shouldn't have said another rude word).

Trevor shouldn't have interfered
with the video,

That's not *Maths Today*,
that's *Neighbours*!

or stolen the school bell.

Hear ye, hear ye!
End of school!
End of school!

When it really was the end of
school, Mr Reece sent for me. I only
had to look at him to know he was
very annoyed.

'Right, Samantha, I told you I didn't want any more trouble and I meant it,' he said. 'That bird is an absolute menace. I don't know where it could have learnt to behave so badly.'

At a Polly-technic!
Hahahaha!

'I warned you before.
I want you to take that
bird home and I don't want
to see it in school again. Now I've
got to take Mr Franks home, because
of his braces. I am **not** pleased.'

Tuesday After School

I picked up my things and got ready
to go home. I was really miserable –
I'd never got into trouble with
Mr Reece before.

Trevor started to open his beak. I
told him to shut up.

'Don't say anything. You're
a cheeky, terrible, wicked,
nasty, rude, awful bird.'

It was the last straw when I
discovered that horrible bird had
hidden my PE kit, I had to go back
to the cloakroom to look for it.

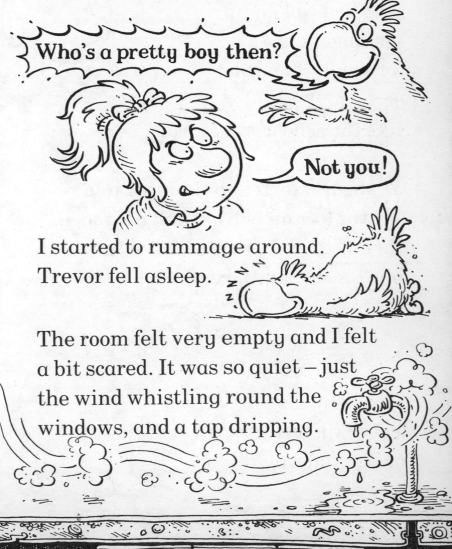

Who's a pretty boy then?

Not you!

I started to rummage around.
Trevor fell asleep.

The room felt very empty and I felt
a bit scared. It was so quiet – just
the wind whistling round the
windows, and a tap dripping.

Suddenly, I heard a scream!

'What was that . . .?'
mumbled Trevor,
who had woken up
for a moment.
'I thought I heard a
scream. It sounded
like the school secretary.'

My heart started to thump. I told
Trevor to stay behind and not move,
then I started to tiptoe down the
big, scary, empty corridor.

At the door of Mrs Palmer's office,
I stopped and peered round.

I saw something which sent a shiver
down my spine . . .

What happened next was just bad luck. I ran full tilt slap bang crash wallop into the tropical fish tank.

What was that?

I thought I heard something!

Like a small girl running full tilt into a tank full of tropical fish!

What?

What did it sound like?

We'd better take a look!

There was nothing I could do to get away – I was in a large pool of water surrounded by rocks and weed, and the general remains of Mr Reece's pride and joy.

Lucky we brought some spare rope!

The burglars pushed me into Mrs Palmer's office. I kicked and struggled but in the end, they tied me up.

Soon Mrs Palmer's office looked like this.

The two burglars decided to go out to dinner.

Suddenly we heard a deep voice which filled the room:

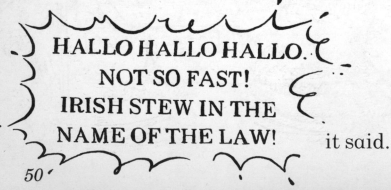

HALLO HALLO HALLO.
NOT SO FAST!
IRISH STEW IN THE
NAME OF THE LAW! it said.

'Whaaaaat!!??' The two burglars both spoke together.

'I said,' said the voice, 'Hallo hallo hallo. Not so fast. I arrest you in the name of the law.'

The burglars were amazed. So were Mrs Palmer and me.

The voice went on: *I must ask you both to put that money on the desk, raise your hands and face the wall. Anything you say may be taken down and read out in the police station!*

'Trousers!' muttered Underdog.

'He didn't mean that,' snapped Moggo. 'He meant to say it's a fair cop, we're guilty.'

We watched as a small green object

whizzed by in a flurry of tissue.

Within seconds, the robbers had
been skilfully blindfolded with
toilet paper.

With one peck, Trevor's beak cut
through Mrs Palmer's ropes.

Another peck and I was free, too.

Trevor took off with the ropes and swooped round and round the robbers until they were trussed up...

... like Egyptian mummies.

The door opened and there stood Mr
Reece. He looked round.

'What on earth is going on?'
said Mr Reece.

Mrs Palmer explained, 'These two terrible men came into school just as you left. They tied me up and started to rob the school. Samantha tried to go for help, but had a nasty accident with the fish tank. Then this brave wonderful marvellous parrot came to our rescue. Thanks to him we still have the dinner money. He's my hero.'

And I explained how Trevor had
imitated a policeman then
blindfolded and tied up the burglars
so they couldn't get away.

Mr Reece
looked at me.

Then he
looked at Trevor.

Trevor put his head on one side.

'Samantha,' said Mr Reece, 'I must
have been wrong about your parrot.
He is obviously a very clever bird.
Congratulations. Who's a pretty
boy, then?'

'I AM!!' roared Trevor.

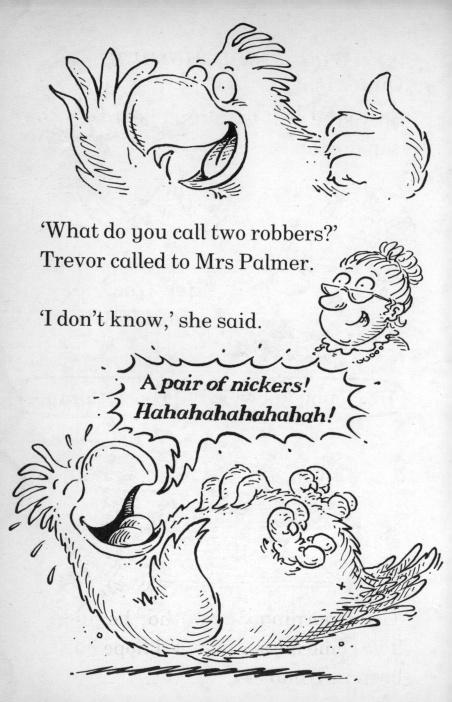

'What do you call two robbers?'
Trevor called to Mrs Palmer.

'I don't know,' she said.

A *pair of nickers!*
Hahahahahahahah!

Wednesday Morning

Early the next morning I heard a 'tap tap tap' on my door.

I opened it and Mr Robinson was standing on the step.

'Good morning, Samantha,' he said, 'I've come for my parrot. I hope he's been no trouble.'

'Oh no,' I said, 'No trouble at all.'

discoveries
that changed the world

Philip Ardagh

Illustrated by Sally Kindberg

MACMILLAN CHILDREN'S BOOKS

First published 2000 by Macmillan Children's Books

This edition published 2006 by Macmillan Children's Books
a division of Macmillan Publishers Limited
20 New Wharf Road, London N1 9RR
Basingstoke and Oxford
www.panmacmillan.com

Associated companies throughout the world

ISBN-13: 978-0-330-44453-8
ISBN-10: 0-330-44453-0

Text copyright © Philip Ardagh 2000, 2006
Illustrations copyright © Sally Kindberg 2000

The right of Philip Ardagh and Sally Kindberg to be identified as the
author and illustrator of this work has been asserted by them in accordance with the
Copyright, Designs and Patents Act 1988.

1 3 5 7 9 8 6 4 2

A CIP catalogue record for this book is available from
the British Library.

Typeset by Nigel Hazle
Printed in China

For my parents,
and about time too.

CONTENTS

DISCOVERIES!

Imagine a world where no one has discovered anaesthetics so if you need your leg amputated, you'll be wide awake and feeling the pain whilst the surgeon saws through your bone . . . or a world where no one has discovered germs, so we've done nothing to stop them spreading. (You might eat off the same old dirty plate, or never have clean sheets.) Imagine a world where we haven't found a way of working out where we are when we're out at sea, and a world where America hasn't been discovered by Europeans. Think of a world with no electricity, no plastics, no knowledge of the fact that atoms themselves can be changed to create terrifying nuclear explosions. In this *WOW* book, we take a look at some of these incredible discoveries and how they've altered just about everything around us. As for the future, we can only guess. Who knows what's out there, waiting to be discovered, perhaps by one of YOU?

PHILIP ARDAGH

SECRETS OF THE UNIVERSE

FEBRUARY 1633, THE PAPAL COURT, ROME

Galileo Galilei has written a book in which he argues that both Heaven and Earth are governed by the same natural laws and are both part of a solar system which, in turn, is part of an even greater universe. Worse than that, he has argued that the Earth is not the centre of this universe and that the Earth revolves around the sun and does NOT remain stationary whilst the sun revolves around it.

This final (and wholly accurate) claim goes totally against the teachings of the Church. He could be put to death for such **heresy**, so reads out a document saying that he was wrong. When he finishes, there are those who claim that he mutters, 'Still it moves' – meaning the Earth around the sun – whatever the Pope and the Holy Catholic Church might think!

HEAVEN AND EARTH

The first true humans were probably too busy looking for food and trying to keep alive to think about big issues such as the shape of the Earth but, once people did take an interest in these matters, they probably assumed that it was well and truly flat. It makes sense, doesn't it? Why should the Earth be any other shape? If it was round, you'd fall off it, wouldn't you? To begin with, people had no idea that the Earth was a planet hanging in space, up there with all the other planets and stars. Why should they? Down here was Earth and up there were the heavens. And that was the end of the story.

NOT THAT FLAT?

Then people must have started to spot clues that the Earth might not be flat after all. The biggest clue of all is the horizon – the line where the land (or the water) appears to join the sky. (The best place to see the horizon is looking out to sea, because there are no hills or trees or buildings in the way.) If you're standing on the quayside watching a ship sailing off out of port and into the distance, whilst your friend is watching the same ship from high in a tower directly above you, you can make two important observations. First, the horizon line between the sea and the sky isn't a straight line. It's slightly curved. Secondly – even if you have equally good eyesight – your friend will see the

ship for longer than you do before it disappears from view. Why? The reason why you can't see the ship any more isn't because it's so far away that it's just a tiny disappearing dot, but because it's gone *over* the horizon. In other words, it's gone over the curve of the Earth. That's also why your friend in the tower can see the ship for longer. Because he's higher up, he can see further over the curve so is, in fact, seeing a different horizon line to you. And why is the horizon line curved, not straight? Because the world is round, not flat.

BACK IT UP

It's a common **misconception** that, until the days of Christopher Columbus and people like him, everyone assumed that the world was flat and that people might one day sail over the edge. But what about Atlas? Not *an* atlas – a book of maps – but *the* Atlas, the ancient Greek god who carried the world on his shoulders. The 'world' was often simply shown as the Earth and the ancient Greeks represented it as the sphere (round object) it is . . . and that was *thousands* of years ago. Many ancient Greek astronomers argued that the Earth hung, stock-still, like a globe on an invisible string, whilst all the stars and planets moved around it. But at least they got the shape right.

ON THE BALL

Then an ancient Greek named Aristarchus of Sàmos came up with an amazing theory: that not only did the Earth turn on its axis – an invisible line running between the

North and South Poles – every twenty-four hours but that it also revolved around the sun, along with all the other planets. What is amazing was that, first, Aristarchus came up with this theory over 2,200 years ago; secondly, few people, if anyone, believed him; and, thirdly, he was right!

GOD'S GRAND DESIGN

Then along came another ancient Greek called Ptolemy about 400 years later – that's still over 1,800 years ago – and produced lots of astrological maps and charts showing a stationary Earth, not the sun, at the centre of things. And it was Ptolemy's view that was believed and taken up by the Christian Church. As far as the Church was concerned, the universe was God's creation and humans were his 'children'. *Of course* He would have placed them at the very centre of the world.

6

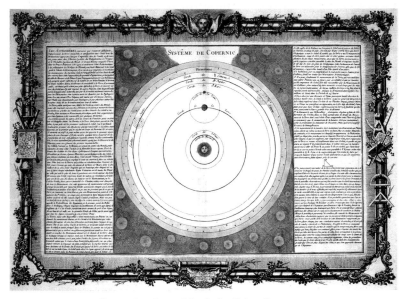

Copernicus's model of the Solar System

The Polish astronomer Nicolaus Copernicus certainly didn't agree. In 1543, he published a book packed full of his discoveries and theories. He hadn't known of the much earlier theories of Aristarchus of Sàmos, but had reached the same conclusions, using astrological observation and mathematics: that the Earth turned around once each day as it moved around the sun, as did all the other planets. This is called the 'heliocentric' system, because

Nicolaus Copernicus, Polish astronomer

Helios was the Greek god of the sun and 'centric' means 'centred'. Galileo Galilei (1564–1642) looked through his nice new telescope, agreed with Copernicus, expressed his views and ended up in the mess we found him in at the beginning of this chapter. But, slowly, people began to realize the truth of such claims. Galileo didn't lose his life, but he was put under house arrest for his 'crimes'.

Galileo Galilei, Italian astronomer and physicist, 1635

STICK TO IT

So here we all are on a round Earth, spinning on its axis between the North and South Poles, and also revolving around the sun but – er – how come we don't fall off? *You* know the answer's an invisible force called gravity, and *I* know that the answer's an invisible force called gravity, but that's only because someone has already discovered the answer for us! That person was Englishman Sir Isaac Newton.

GETTING THE BALL ROLLING

Galileo himself had done experiments on dropping objects but hadn't stopped to consider *why* things fall in the first place. He was more interested in disproving the popularly held belief that heavy objects fall faster than light ones. In other words, he wanted to disprove the belief that if a heavy object and a light object are dropped at the same time, the heavier object will hit the ground first. The reason why this was so widely believed was because it apparently seemed easy to prove: drop a brick and a feather together and we all know that the brick will hit the ground first. Galileo argued that this had nothing to do with weight. And, once again, he was right. The reason why the feather falls slower has to do with other factors, such as **air resistance**. By rolling solid balls of different weights and sizes down a ramp and timing their descent, he found that they all took the same length of time to reach the bottom. In other words: drop two solid balls of different weights, and under ideal conditions – without wind resistance – they'd hit the ground at the same time. Roll them down a ramp and they actually do!

An American astronaut was able to put Galileo's theory to the test over 300 years later, by carrying out the experiment on the moon. Because the moon has no atmosphere, there's no air resistance. The astronaut dropped two balls of different weights and size, and, with the moon's gravity being far less than Earth's, they fell very slowly to the ground . . . hitting it at the same time. Which brings us neatly back to gravity.

GRAVITY

Whether Isaac Newton really did start thinking about gravity after he got a bonk on the head from an apple falling from a tree, or whether that's just a good story, understanding gravity was certainly a remarkable achievement. He worked out that there is a 'force of attraction' between any two objects (you and the Earth, for example), and that this force is proportional to the product of the two

Sir Isaac Newton, 1689

masses, not the total **mass** of these objects (with the enormous Earth's pull on you much greater than your pull on it). Going back to the brick and the feather, the reason why they would fall at the same rate (if there was no air resistance) is because the *total* mass of Earth **x** brick is almost exactly the same as that of Earth **x** feather.

THE LAWS OF THE UNIVERSE

Newton also made many other important discoveries and observations. For example, he proved that white light – ordinary sunlight – is made up of the colours of the rainbow (a **spectrum** of different-coloured light) and that the pull of the moon does indeed control the Earth's tides (something Galileo had suspected). He is also well-known for his three laws of motion, which explain how moving objects behave (even when they run into each other). Newton put together all his discoveries and theories into a book called the *Principia* (1687) which, even today, is still regarded by many to be one of the greatest scientific books ever written. It contained everything from the fact that the Earth didn't orbit the sun in a circle, but an oval (elliptical) orbit, to why pendulums swing the way they do!

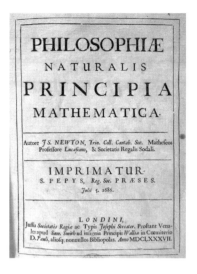

Principia Mathematica, 1687

SO WHAT?

It's thanks to the dedication, commitment and discoveries of men such as Galileo and Newton that the age of true science was born and that people really began to make sense of the world around them, understanding why things happened in the way they did. Once people could understand the basic principles and natural laws of the workings of the universe, then they could begin to use this knowledge to invent new products and to develop new ideas for the benefit of humankind. Newton's view of the universe – sometimes described as being the 'clockwork mechanics' view – still helps to explain gravity, motion and much of what goes on around us. In the twentieth century, however, German-born Albert Einstein was about to turn some of those Newtonian theories on their heads!

RELATIVITY

14 MARCH 1879, ULM, GERMANY

Pauline has just given birth to her first child. It's a healthy boy and both Pauline and her husband, Hermann, are delighted. Hermann is an electrical engineer at a time when electrical

products are a new and exciting area to work in. Next year, he'll be moving his family to Munich to team up with his brother Jacob to make electrical equipment. Who knows? This newborn baby boy might grow up to be a fine electrical engineer himself, one day. He might even take over the company. They'll call him Albert. That's it: Mr and Mrs Hermann Einstein and their son Albert. Who knows what the future might bring young Albert Einstein?

Albert Einstein

IT'S ALL RELATIVE

Imagine you're standing at the edge of the road, holding a machine that records the speed of passing objects. If a car is driven past at 60 mph (miles per hour) the machine will, of course, register 60 mph. Now imagine you're in a car being driven at 40 mph, and you stick your machine out of the window at the car driving at 60 mph alongside. What speed will the machine register now? Twenty miles per hour, because *relative to the car you're in* (going 40 mph) the car going 60 mph is only going 20 mph faster.

STRAIGHT LIGHT

The speed of light (unlike the speeds of the cars in the imaginary experiment above) is *constant*. In other words, if you're standing still when you point the speed-recording machine at a beam of light or if you're in a rocket car travelling at 600 mph, the speed will always be recorded as 186,000 miles per second. Not miles per hour. Per *second*. (This is an approximate figure; a more accurate one is 299,792,458 metres per second in a **vacuum**.) We know that light always travels in a straight line (at the speed of light) because if it could bend and flow like water, there wouldn't be shadows – which are simply the absence of light. (It would go round corners and everything would be bright!)

SEEING THE LIGHT!

Albert Einstein, the brilliant scientist who is now everyone's idea of an absolute genius, observed that the acceleration (speeding up) of an object appeared to bend light. But, because he knew that light could only travel in straight lines and *couldn't* be bent, he knew that there must be something else going on. His conclusion was remarkably simple, yet the implications were mind-boggling: light itself wasn't bending, but the time and space through which it was travelling was! This is how he worked it out . . .

SPACE AND TIME

Speed is measured by the time it takes for an object to travel a certain distance (or, to put it more scientifically: distance divided by time). So, if light can only travel at one constant speed through space, yet it appears to bend sometimes, it must be the time and space that have been distorted, and which, in turn, appear to distort light.

THE GRAVITY OF IT ALL!

Now imagine you're an astronaut in a spaceship up in space. You're weightless and floating about because you're away from the Earth and the Earth's gravity. It's the force of gravity that keeps our feet – and everything around us – firmly on the ground. Up in your spaceship, you don't have that. If the spaceship suddenly accelerates, though, you'll find yourself flat on the spaceship floor and – if it's going really fast – the force of acceleration will be so great that you won't even be able to stand up. If, however, your spaceship is accelerating at a nice, constant 9.8 metres per second, it would be like being in a room back on Earth. The pull of the acceleration would exactly match gravity. Because, under these conditions, gravity and acceleration are the equivalent of each other, this is called the principle of equivalence. So, Albert Einstein argued, if acceleration – of, say, a speeding spaceship – can bend space and time, and gravity behaves like acceleration, then *gravity* is, in truth, space and time (space–time) (And he worked all of this out before there were even such things as spacecraft.) So what we think of as acceleration due to gravity is actually the bending of space–time by the gravity created by a mass (such as our own Earth). Einstein reasoned, therefore, that a large object such as the sun would attract something as weightless as light, bending the time and space around it.

A BENDY UNIVERSE

Before Einstein came along and changed everyone's way of thinking, most physicists believed in the science of the universe as put forward by another brilliant person: Sir Isaac (see the Secrets of the Universe chapter). The way Newton saw it, the universe was an ordered place. Einstein realized that it was very different. Imagine a trampoline with a grid of nice straight lines drawn on the flat canvas, representing light travelling in straight lines, at a constant speed, through time and space. Now imagine dropping a large ball in the middle of the trampoline and then another, and then another. When you jump on a trampoline the canvas bends and stretches.

It's the same if you drop something heavy on it. These balls will pull down on the canvas of the trampoline, distorting the once-straight lines so that they're all bent and stretched too. The nearer the lines are to a ball, the more wonky they will have become. This was how Einstein saw the universe. The balls were the stars and planets whose gravity – acting like acceleration – was distorting space and time.

BUT WHAT DOES IT MEAN?

The Earth, the sun, the moon and the stars all have gravity of different strengths, so they are bending space and time in different ways. And what does this mean? It means that, up in space, time can go faster or slower relative to time down here on Earth. Why? Because if gravity and acceleration can bend time, then 'bent time' will be slower than 'straight time', since a straight line is the quickest way to get between two points. (So, in theory, an astronaut could come back from the deep reaches of space to find everyone has aged whilst he hasn't – or the other way around!) If you understand this much, then you understand the very basics of Einstein's Theories of Relativity.

A 3-D WORLD?

We're all aware of living in a three-dimensional world. A very thin line has one basic dimension: length. A square has two basic dimensions: height and width. A real box (as opposed to a drawing of one) has three dimensions: length, width and depth (the front-to-back measurement). If a drawing looks very flat we say it's very two-dimensional. If it looks very lifelike, we say that it looks amazingly three-dimensional. Einstein was thinking in *four* dimensions, an idea first proposed in 1908 by a Russian-German named Hermann Minkowski. That fourth element is space–time: three dimensions in space (as described) and the fourth in time. It is this space–time that is actually bent by gravity and that can only really be shown using mathematical equations.

SUPER SCIENTIST

Einstein became a superstar, although not so much in the scientific world to begin with but among ordinary people. He went on tours around the world and was greeted by thousands of cheering fans. The only person anywhere near as popular was Charlie Chaplin. Chaplin is supposed to have said that he was famous because everyone could understand him (in the screen role of a little tramp with a good heart), whereas Einstein was famous because no one could understand him (or his theory, at least)! Many scientists, meanwhile, were reluctant to accept just how brilliant he was. Many didn't think him a 'proper scientist' at first. (When he published his first theory, he was working in the Swiss Patent Office!) Scientists are still testing important parts of Einstein's theories, but so far nobody has proved him wrong.

THE LEGACY

Albert Einstein's Theories of Relativity have turned our understanding of the world on its head. In fact, he published his discoveries and conclusions in two separate papers: *The Special Theory of Relativity* in 1905 and *The General Theory of Relativity* in 1916. (It was in his *Special Theory* that he included the now infamous equation $E=mc^2$, where E is energy, m is mass and c^2 – c squared – is the speed of light multiplied by itself.) Einstein's work not only proved that some of Newton's Laws (the very foundation on which much of modern science was built) were not the full story, but also suggested that – in theory at least – time travel, of sorts, is possible. He even got scientists seriously thinking in the fourth – space–time – dimension! Many are still trying to work out all the implications of these amazing scientific discoveries.

THE POWER OF THE ATOM

6 AUGUST 1945, HIROSHIMA, JAPAN

On the orders of the Supreme Allied Headquarters, in a bid to hasten the end of the Second World War in which over 25 million people will have lost their lives, the world's first atomic bomb is dropped on the city by the crew of the *Enola Gay* of the United States Air Force, with the energy of up to 15 kilotons of TNT. President Harry S. Truman of the USA announces, 'We won the race of discovery against the Germans. We have used it to shorten the agony of war.' Reports will later state that 129,558 Japanese men, women and children were killed, injured or missing, their city flattened and nearly 176,000 survivors made homeless. Later, tens of thousands will die of radiation burns and sickness. The theory of the awesome, destructive power of the atom has become an explosive fact.

A replica of 'Little Boy', the atomic bomb dropped on Hiroshima

19

CHOP! CHOP!

Long, long ago in ancient Greece there were the first real professional thinkers – called philosophers – and one thing a number of them put their minds to was chopping things up. They didn't *actually* chop anything up, you understand. They just thought about it. After all, that was their job. Some argued that, **in theory**, you could go on chopping something up into smaller and smaller pieces for ever. In other words, if humans had brilliant eyesight and small enough, sharp enough tools, you would *never* reach a stage where something was too small to be cut up further. Other philosophers disagreed. They argued that you must reach a point where you couldn't cut something up any more.

TINY PARTICLES

If that was the case, they argued, what you were left with – these smallest particles that couldn't be cut any smaller – must be the very particles that went together to make up the object. The earliest record of this theory dates all the way back to **c** 400 BC (about 2,400 years ago) to two philosophers named Democritus and Leucippus. They thought that these tiny particles probably came in different shapes. (Perhaps, for example, spicy food particles were spiky, which is why they pricked your tongue?) Although the idea was taken up by a later ancient Greek philosopher, Epicurus, it wasn't until over 2,200 years later that someone gave a name to those tiny particles and developed a fully fledged idea about them. That person's name was John Dalton, and the name he gave the particles was 'atoms'.

THE EXTRAORDINARY MR DALTON

John Dalton in later life

John Dalton was an unusual man. A **colour-blind** English Quaker son of a weaver, he became a teacher at the age of twelve and remained one, in one form or another, for the rest of his life. From 1787, he kept a written record of the weather almost every single day up until he died in 1844 (some 200,000 observations and 57 years later)! It was in 1807 that Dalton published his Atomic Theory, the main ideas of which were:

- All matter is made up of tiny particles, which he named atoms (from the Greek 'atomos', meaning 'that which cannot be divided').
- Atoms cannot be made, divided or destroyed.
- Atoms of the same **element** are identical.
- Chemical reactions are a result of atoms rearranging themselves.
- In **compounds**, atoms can join together to make larger particles.

Dalton later revised his original theory to suggest that an atom *could*, in theory at least, be split into even smaller particles – in other words, that atoms were themselves made up of what we now call **subatomic** particles. He was right. His only real mistake was the belief that all atoms in an element were the same – but that didn't stop his Atomic Theory being mind-blowingly brilliant and changing the way scientists thought about how everything in the universe was made.

MODEL MANIA!

Over the next 100 years or so, a number of scientists produced a number of different models to show how they imagined an atom was made up. British scientist J. J.

J. J. Thomson

Sir Ernest Rutherford's laboratory, early 20th century

Thomson came up with the 'plum-pudding' model, which looked like an old-fashioned, round Christmas pud (hence the name) but, instead of fruit, it was embedded with representations of negatively charged subatomic grains. It was Thomson who actually went beyond theory to practice, and discovered both negatively and positively charged particles using a piece of equipment called a cathode ray tube (more advanced versions of these are now used in the screen in television sets). New Zealand-born Ernest Rutherford's model had these negatively charged particles (which he called electrons) circling a positively charged **nucleus** at the centre. Then, in 1932, James Chadwick

discovered that the nucleus also contained neutral (neither positively nor negatively charged) neutrons, as well as the positively-charged protons.

AN IDEA OF SIZE

When reading (or writing) about atoms, it's important to remember just how teeny-weenie they really are. They are small divided by small – then even smaller still. Imagine a grain of sand in the palm of your hand or, if you live near a beach like I do, why not actually put a grain of sand in your hand? Now, that's small, isn't it? Yup, but it's made up of thousands of even smaller atoms. In fact, if each of the atoms in that grain of sand grew to the size of that itsy-bitsy, teeny-weenie grain of sand, the grain of sand itself would suddenly be almost 10 km (6.21 miles) wide, and your hand would be s-q-u-a-s-h-e-d. *That's* an idea of just how small the heroes of this chapter are!

THE HEART OF THE ATOM

Now I can tell you that an atom's nucleus is 10,000 times smaller still! And even more incredible, the nucleus itself is made up of even smaller particles! No two elements contain the same number of protons (those positively charged subatomic particles) in their nuclei. This means that an element can be identified by counting the number of protons in the nucleus. This number is called the element's atomic number. Its atomic mass (also a number) is made up of the number of protons in an atom's nucleus – its atomic number – *plus* the number of neutrons.

RADIOACTIVITY

Antoine Becquerel, c 1890s

The bigger an atom, the more likely it is to break up. Any atom with an atomic number above 83 has *so many* protons in its nucleus that it becomes unstable and begins to come apart. As it falls to pieces, it becomes radioactive, giving off one of three different types of radiation: alpha, beta or gamma. It was the French scientist Henri Becquerel who discovered radioactivity in 1896, but he didn't know what it was, or even what to call it. It is thanks to Polish scientist Marie Curie and her French husband Pierre that so much was learned about it so quickly. Marie discovered two radioactive elements. The first she called polonium, after Poland. The second she named radium, and she and Pierre came up with the term 'radioactivity'. Sadly, Pierre Curie was killed by a cart when crossing the road, but not before

Marie and Pierre Curie

he and Marie had won the **Nobel Prize** for Physics in 1903. Marie went on to win the Nobel Prize for Chemistry in 1911. Their daughter, Irène, also became a scientist working on radioactivity. She too won a Nobel Prize in 1935, the year after her mother died.

FISSION

There are two ways of starting a nuclear reaction (the process of creating radiation) and freeing the atom's incredible power. The first is called fission. This was explained by the German Otto Hahn and the Austrian Lise Meitner in the 1930s. They began by working together but, following the rise of **Nazism**, Meitner fled to

Model of Fermi's 'Chicago Pile No. 1' reactor, 1942

Sweden to avoid persecution, because she'd been classified Jewish. Hahn sent Meitner the results of his latest experiments on radiation and she showed them to her nephew, another 'Otto', this time Otto Frisch. This collaboration resulted in Hahn unleashing the amazing power of fission to the world in 1938: when neutrons were fired at a nucleus, causing it to break into at least two parts, incredible energy was released. By 1942, Italian-born Enrico Fermi had built a nuclear reactor in Chicago, generating electricity

BOOM

BIFF
BIFF

with fission. It was the first in the world. (In fact, Fermi had actually achieved fission in 1934, but no one accepted what it was until Hahn's paper was published!)

A-BOMB

Following the outbreak of the Second World War, the now world-famous Albert Einstein – who was, by then, working in the USA – was very worried that the Germans might discover a way of using nuclear fission to make a new type of bomb. The solution, he argued – with a group of other scientists – was to develop an A-bomb (atom bomb) first and wrote a letter to the US president saying so. As a result of this and other pressures, the US government set up the Manhattan Project in 1943, but Einstein played no part in it. Many other scientists, including Lise Meitner, refused to work on the project. They believed that the destruction caused by the A-bomb would be too great. The director of the Manhattan Project, at Los Alamos, New Mexico, was Robert J. Oppenheimer. Following the dropping of the bomb on the Japanese city of Hiroshima on 5 August 1945 (Germany, Japan's ally, had already surrendered), another A-bomb was dropped on Nagasaki on 9 August. By 14 August, the Japanese had surrendered and the war was over. Many Japanese people who survived the blasts died of radiation burns and sickness, the result of **nuclear fallout**.

FUSION

Even before the bombs were dropped, scientists realized that there was, in theory at least, another kind of nuclear reaction: nuclear fusion. This was where two nuclei are forced together to create one big nucleus. By the end of the war, US and **Soviet** scientists were working on a bomb, **independently**, combining both types of reaction: the fission-fusion bomb. Also called the H-bomb, or thermonuclear bomb, this device contained an A-bomb surrounded by a substance containing hydrogen. When the A-bomb was exploded by fission, it would cause the hydrogen nuclei to fuse together to create a second, far greater, fusion reaction. Both the USA and the Soviet Union carried out controlled explosions with H-bombs in the early 1950s. Since then, more and more complicated nuclear weapons have been created, including **inter-continental ballistic missiles**. So far, fortunately, thermonuclear weapons haven't actually been fired or dropped in a real war.

AND THEN?

Today, there are roughly 350 nuclear power stations, supplying about 20 per cent of the world's energy using nuclear fission. These power stations use a fourth type of radiation – remember alpha, beta and gamma back on page 25 – called neutron radiation. Radiation is also used to treat cancer. Radiation treatment changes the subatomic particles in cancerous cells, making them harmless. A dose of gamma radiation can make most types of food stay 'fresher' longer too. This is called irradiation. An irradiated peach, for example, will still look fresh two weeks after an untreated peach has gone mouldy.

FRESH!
(or is it?)

There are many people who are against not only nuclear weapons, but *all* human uses of radioactivity. They argue that the possible dangers far outweigh the benefits of unleashing the power of the atom. What's certainly true is that, even if nuclear weapons are never fired in anger and are simply used as a deterrent or a threat, a world with nuclear weapons is a very different place to how it was before.

ELECTRICITY

20 FEBRUARY 1962, INSIDE 'FRIENDSHIP 7' CAPSULE, SOMEWHERE ABOVE EARTH

Astronaut John Glenn is nearing the completion of his Project Mercury Gemini mission and has become the first American to orbit the Earth in space. He will orbit the planet three times in just under five hours and cover about 81,000 miles. As he passes over Australia, he is greeted with the twinkling of thousands upon thousands of light bulbs as towns and cities light their streetlamps and house lights to send him their good wishes – using the power of electricity.

AMBER

It was those brainy ancient Greeks – yup, them again – who noticed that if you rubbed a piece of amber, little pieces of material would become attracted to it and even stick to it. One of the first was probably Thales of Miletus in c 600 BC. Amber looks like a transparent gem but is, in fact, fossilized tree **sap**. You can tell it was once a liquid because you can often see insects in pieces of amber, trapped when it was still a gooey liquid. (And its colour? Why, amber of course. No prizes for guessing where the

name for *that* colour came from.) What the ancient Greeks had discovered when rubbing amber was what we now call static electricity.

SHOCKINGLY STATIC

Static electricity doesn't just happen with amber. Rub a balloon on your hair and it will stick to the ceiling. That's another example of static electricity. Occasionally you might go to hold someone's hand – don't go all soppy here – and see a spark pass between you, or feel a little 'shock', especially if you're walking on a nylon carpet. That's yet another example of static electricity. You can also sometimes build up static electricity when stroking a cat, particularly if it's a long-haired one like my cat, Beany. The word 'electric' was invented by an English doctor named William Gilbert in 1600. He chose it because it came from the Greek word 'elektron' meaning . . . guess. Go on, guess. It was Greek for amber. William Gilbert, an Englishman, was very interested in electrical and magnetic **phenomena**.

CHARGE!

The first machine especially designed to produce an electric charge – a generator – was described in 1672 in the writings of a German physicist called Otto von Guericke, but it was the Frenchman Charles François de Cisternay Du Fay who made the big breakthrough. He discovered that there were two, clearly different types of electrical charge: positive charges (+) and negative charges (–).

Otto von Guericke, 1649

SO WHAT IS ELECTRICITY?

Electricity is, in fact, a form of energy caused by the moving of positively and negatively charged subatomic particles. With electrical charges, dissimilar charges (such as + – or – +) attract each other – as with the amber attracting the pieces of material, or the balloon being attracted to the ceiling and sticking to it – and similar charges (such as + + or – –) repel each other, pushing each other apart. This is usually stated as: 'Like charges repel. Unlike charges attract.' Electricity can be made to flow down a wire, for example, because the charged particles are being attracted to an opposite charge – it's pulling them along, creating an electric current.

A JAR OF ELECTRICITY, PLEASE

A condenser is something that stores electricity, ready to release it. The earliest condenser is now known as the Leyden jar and was invented by two people, quite independently of each other, in about 1754 – neither of whom was called Leyden. One was a Dutch physicist called Pieter van Musschenbroek and the other was a Pomeranian

A Leyden jar, 1746

called Georg von Kleist. Pieter van Musschenbroek worked at the University of *Leyden* and Ewald, which is where the 'Leyden' name comes from. The original Leyden jar was a glass jar filled with water. In the neck of the jar was a stopper with a nail (or possibly a wire) sticking through both ends, the bottom part in the water. The jar could be charged with electricity by holding the nail sticking from the top of the stopper to a generator – something that generates (or makes) electricity. Once moved from the electrical source, the jar was now stored with electricity. How could you tell? By holding the jar in one hand and touching the nail coming through the top of the stopper with the other – the electricity in the jar was then discharged through your arm, giving you a nasty shock! Your body was acting as a **conductor**, and I don't mean the types you might find in an orchestra or selling you a ticket on a bus.

LIGHTNING

The multi-talented American Benjamin Franklin – scientist, publisher, author and statesperson – was fascinated by electricity. He wanted to prove that atmospheric electricity (in other words thunder and lightning) was the same kind of electricity as a static electric charge. In 1747, he came up with an experiment involving a kite, which might help to prove it, and his idea was published in London. As a result, it was successfully carried out in both England and France

Benjamin Franklin

before he actually put it to the test himself in the USA in 1752. The experiment involved flying a kite in a thunderstorm with a metal key tied to a wet string. The lightning hit the string and the electric charge flowed down towards Franklin. (Some people were later killed trying this experiment, **SO DON'T EVEN THINK ABOUT GIVING IT A GO YOURSELF**!!) He then invented the lightning rod (also known as a lightning conductor) for tall buildings. Attached to tall buildings, these rods create a **low-resistance** path for the lightning – so the electric charge runs down the rod to the ground rather than damaging the buildings. For this, and other works, he not only received honorary degrees from the University of St Andrews and the University of Oxford, but also became a fellow of the Royal Society of London and, in 1753, was awarded the Society's very shiny and very important 'Copley Medal'. (Franklin developed a theory that electricity was a 'fluid' that existed in all matter which we now, of course, know is wrong. But, hey, we can't all be right all of the time.)

A lightning conductor, c1749

VOLTS AND AMPS

André-Marie Ampère, 1810

Another man greatly interested in 'atmospheric electricity' was the Italian physicist Alessandro Volta (1745–1827). He also invented what became known as the Voltaic Pile (c 1800), which produced a source of electricity. It was really the first efficient **battery**. The Emperor Napoleon (boss of France and of 'Not tonight, Josephine' fame) was so impressed with Volta's

Alessandro Volta, c 1810

work that he made him a count. The electrical unit the **volt** – as in 'DANGER 30,000 VOLTS' – was also named after him in his honour. Another electrical unit, the **amp**, was named after Frenchman André Ampère. He worked on the connection between electricity and magnetism: electromagnetism, and he made many impressive discoveries. One such discovery involved experiments with two conductors lined up parallel to each other. When an electrical current was passed through the conductors in the same direction, the conductors attracted each other – in other words, they pulled towards each other. But if the electrical currents were passed in the opposite direction, the conductors repelled each other – pushed each other further apart. (The **watt**, by the way, as in 60-watt light bulb, was named after the Scottish engineer James Watt, whom you can read about in *WOW: Inventions that changed the world.* In fact, he had little to do with electricity, except that it can be generated using the steam power from his steam engines.)

FARADAY'S FIELD DAY

Yet another electrical unit is called the **farad**, and it is named after the British scientist Michael Faraday (1791–1867), but it isn't as commonly used as volt, amp or watt. Faraday was the son of a blacksmith and didn't get much of an education. He could, however, read; this skill came in very handy when he became an apprentice to a London bookbinder. As well as binding the books, he managed to read a number of the scientific ones, and they captured his imagination. He was soon conducting experiments of his own in his spare time. His early interest

Faraday in his laboratory, 1831

was in chemistry and he was eventually taken on as an assistant to a well-respected scientist called Sir Humphry Davy. He got the job by attending one of Sir Humphry's lectures and sending him some of his notes afterwards. Sir Humphry was mightily impressed, and Faraday ended up going on a European tour with him in 1813. It was

Sir Humphry Davy, 1801

Faraday's experiments with electromagnetism in the 1820s and 1830s that were his greatest triumph. Amongst other things (and he did make many important discoveries), he discovered that if a wire is passed through a magnetic field – the area affected by a magnet – an electric current passes down that wire. This phenomenon is called 'electromagnetic induction'. The reason why it's such a big deal is because it ultimately led to the invention of the huge electricity generators that are the source of the electricity used to light, heat and power our homes.

LET THERE BE LIGHT

That's the thing about electricity. Once so much was found out about it, once it was *understood*, it could be used to heat, light and power whole cities and to change the world beyond recognition. In the past, people'd had to rely on candles and oil lamps for light, and wood, coal and coke

39

fires for warmth. Then came gas lighting, in the streets and in the home, along with gas fires for warmth. The gas was piped into houses. It was poisonous so, if it leaked, it could either poison you or cause an explosion and blow up you *and* your home! It needed to be lit with a naked flame to give off light and warmth, so it was potentially dangerous in that way too. Electricity changed all that. To begin with, a few 'important' buildings had arc lights, where an arc of electricity sparked between two pieces of carbon. These were more for show than any great practical use. They were incredibly bright but burnt out very quickly and didn't cast light over a very big area. Then came the light bulb.

A BRIGHT IDEA

Swan's electric filament, 1878–1879

The light bulb was invented by Englishman Joseph Swan in 1878, after twenty years' hard work, and – a little later – by inventor and invention-developer, American Thomas Edison (who patented over 1,000 in-ventions and also appears in *WOW: Inventions that Changed the World*). Although Swan got there first, Edison accused Swan of stealing HIS idea! A legal wrangle followed and, eventually, the two men formed the Edison and Swan Electric Company. (Swan may have invented the bulb first, but Edison was the more famous, so he made sure that, at least, his *name* came before Swan's!) On New Year's Eve 1879, the streets and houses of Menlo Park – the village where Edison had his laboratories – were lit with electric light. By September 1881, the world's first electricity power station opened in Pearl Street, New York.

Edison's electric filament, 1878–1879

A SHINING BEACON

Today, electricity is one of the most important tools used by humankind, and not just for heating, lighting and cooking. Electric fences keep livestock in their fields. Electricity powers the computer I'm typing these words on right now. It powers the alarms that protect property, the traffic lights that control the flow of cars, and everything from telephones and the Internet to aeroplanes' flight

41

systems and the radar machines that track the planes in the sky. Look around you. Discovering the power of electricity and harnessing that power has changed the face of the world. Astronaut John Glenn can testify to that. He saw it with his own eyes from space.

THE NEW WORLD

By proclamation of Benjamin Harrison, the 23rd President of the United States of America, the first pledge of allegiance to the flag is proclaimed in schools throughout the land. The wording of the pledge, which will later be slightly revised, is: 'I pledge allegiance to my flag and to the republic for which it stands: one nation, indivisible, with liberty and justice for all.' And the reason for choosing this date to first state the pledge? It's Columbus Day, in memory of Christopher Columbus, the man who discovered America four hundred years previously, in 1492. But, of course, he didn't really discover North America. Did he?

LAND OF OPPORTUNITY

Not all discoveries that changed the world were scientific. The discovery by Europeans of the Americas   north and south – has made a huge impact on history and the world as we know it. Known by explorers and settlers as the New World, the Americas were only new to them, of course. To the people who already lived there, they didn't need to be 'discovered'. It had been home to them and their ancestors for at least 20,000 years! The sheer size, riches and opportunities offered by the New World made it irresistible to those who found it.

CHRISTOPHER COLUMBUS

For a long, long time, Christopher Columbus was famous for being the first European to discover North America. Then he became famous for being the man who *wasn't* really the first European to discover America, but whom people often *thought* was. So how did all this confusion come about? Christopher Columbus's real name wasn't really Christopher Columbus, for starters. It was Cristoforo Colombo. He was born in the independent city of Genoa, so would be what we now think of as Italian. He got the money for his famous expeditions from Spain, however. His **patron** was Queen Isabella of Castile. Columbus was looking for a quick route to Asia but, in 1492, ended up in the Bahamas, landing on a number of islands that we now call San Salvador, Cuba, the Dominican Republic and Haiti – but *he* still assumed that he was in Asian seas.

SOME SERIOUS CONFUSION

The nearest Columbus actually came to setting foot on North American soil was a year later when, in 1493, he stopped off at Puerto Rico (which, today, is officially part of the USA), after which he set up a colony called Isabella near what is now named Cape Isabella, in the Dominican Republic. He did 'discover' mainland South America, though, when his third voyage took him to Venezuela and the mouth of the mighty Orinoco River. To begin with, Columbus had been given a friendly greeting by the indigenous peoples ('natives') wherever he went. But they soon discovered that these European visitors weren't visitors at all, but were intending to stay and were often harsh and cruel. When Columbus kidnapped large numbers of natives in 1495 and sent them to Spain to be sold as slaves, Queen Isabella sent them back, ordering they be released!

THE CABOT CONNECTION

Probably the first European of that era to step on to genuine North American ground – in what is now Canada and not the USA – was John Cabot, who set sail from Bristol in England in 1497. He even sailed along the New England coast. Before any English readers leap up and down shouting, 'YES! Ya boo sucks to you, Columbus!', I should quickly add that Cabot's real name was Giovanni Caboto and, like Columbus, he was born in what is now Italy. He, however, led an *English* expedition and his discovery was what later led to Britain claiming North America as a British colony.

SOUTH AMERICAN RICHES

Following the European discovery of the New World, there were numerous Spanish expeditions and conquests from 1500 onwards, mainly centred on South America (which is why so many languages in the region today are variations of Spanish). One of the most famous **conquistadors** was Hernando Cortés, who destroyed the Aztecs in Mexico. The Aztecs had never seen people on horses and were amazed by the Spanish soldiers but, unknown to either side, an even greater threat was the diseases the conquistadors brought with them. The Aztecs had no immunity to foreign diseases and thousands and thousands died from smallpox and other ailments. Cortés and others weren't only interested in claiming land for their sovereign and power for themselves, though. They'd discovered that South America was rich with gold treasure, and there were rumours of much more.

UNSETTLED SETTLERS

The French and the English, meanwhile, centred most of their efforts on exploring North America. Englishman Sir Walter Raleigh and the very first English **colonists** set off for North America in 1585 and settled on Roanoke Island, off the coast of what is now North Carolina. Like the

Spanish in South America, they seemed more interested in finding gold than settling down and creating a new community. Raleigh's second batch of colonists set off in 1857 and also settled on Roanoke Island, which he now named Virginia, after his **sovereign**, Elizabeth I, the Virgin Queen – and it shouldn't be confused with any later US states of that name. The colony was governed by map-maker John White, whose daughter Ellinor was married to one of his staff, Ananias Dare. Ellinor gave birth to a little girl on 18 August 1587. They called her Virginia, after the colony, and she was the very first person of English parents to be born in North America. John White returned to England for supplies. He didn't come back to Virginia Island until 1590 – to find himself in the heart of one of America's greatest mysteries, still unsolved to this day. All the colonists had disappeared and they were never found. The island is now in an area called Dare County, in memory of little Virginia Dare.

HERE TO STAY

The first permanent, successful English colony to be set up in North America was in Jamestown (now in the state of Virginia) on 14 May 1607. Though named after King James I, who succeeded to the throne of England after the death of childless Queen Elizabeth, Jamestown was run by the Virginia Company of London (rather than being an official English royal province). In the beginning, it was a disaster. Thousands of colonists died of disease and starvation and in fights with the native North Americans! Finally, in 1624, the English crown took control of the colony.

SLAVERY

One of the 'great' discoveries in the New World was tobacco, and the demand for it in Europe was so great that more and huge plantations sprang up in North America. So many people were needed to pick the tobacco that, by the end of the seventeenth century, English colonists were importing huge numbers of black slaves from Africa – ancestors of many of today's African Americans. The North American slave trade was born.

THE FRIENDLY FRENCH

The French, meanwhile, had set up much smaller, better-organized colonies, whose colonists on the whole got on far better with the local people, trading furs. They founded Quebec in Canada and controlled areas around the St Lawrence and Mississippi Rivers. The state of Louisiana was colonized by them in the early eighteenth century and was originally named Louisiane after King Louis XIV by the French explorer René-Robert Cavelier, sieur (lord) de La Salle, in 1682.

THE DUTCH EAST INDIA COMPANY

The Dutch, meanwhile, based their claim to certain North American territory on discoveries made by an Englishman on their behalf. Though English, Henry Hudson worked for the Dutch East India Company. In 1609, he sailed into what is now New York Bay and explored the river that is now called the Hudson after him. In 1625, the Dutch set up a colony called New Amsterdam, after the old Amsterdam in the Netherlands. Today, it's better known as New York, after the old York in England!

THOSE PILGRIM PARENTS

Probably the most famous of all the settlers in the New World were those who became known as the Pilgrim Fathers (though there were plenty of mothers and mothers-to-be too, so Pilgrim Parents would be more accurate). These were **low church** Puritans from England, who were being given a very tough time by King Charles I (who later got his head chopped off). In the end, a group of Puritans decided that enough was enough and, on 16 September 1620, 102 of them set sail from Plymouth in their ship, the *Mayflower*. They reached North America on 21 November 1620, passing Cape Cod and dropping anchor at what later became Provincetown, Massachusetts. Still on board, 41 of the adult male passengers signed the 'Mayflower Compact' – a set of rules to live by which was, in fact, the first written American **constitution**. Today, there's a big monument there to commemorate this piece of history, but this wasn't where they settled. After searching for the best spot, they upped anchor, landed near the tip of Cape Cod and founded Plymouth Colony on 21 December.

A WHOLE NEW WORLD

So how did the discovery of the Americas by Europeans change the world? Beyond recognition. England's grip over its North American colonies grew tighter and tighter until the American War of Independence (1775–83) led to part of North America breaking free and the formation of the United States of America. Then came the get-rich-quick gold rush of 1848/9, then – from 1861–65 – the American Civil War and, later, the USA's involvement in the First and Second World Wars and its emergence as a world superpower. Now *the* superpower. The descendants of these European settlers, and those who have emigrated to the USA since, make up the population of the most powerful and influential country the world has ever known.

THE TRUE DISCOVERERS?

But, if not Columbus or Cabot, who was the first European to discover the New World? Amazingly, the answer probably goes back over a thousand years to a trader from Iceland called Bjarni Herjólfsson who, in 986, reported seeing what was probably the coastline of the

American continent. The honour of being the first Europeans to actually set foot in Amcrica should probably go to the Vikings. Leif Ericson – son of the famous Viking Eric the Red – reported he'd visited a place he called 'Wineland' somewhere between what we now call Labrador and New England. Archaeological evidence in Newfoundland suggests this was a strong possibility. The Vikings had discovered the New World nearly 500 years before Columbus or Cabot came close. Which means that it wasn't really such a 'new' New World, after all!

LONGITUDE

19 JANUARY 1762, JAMAICA, WEST INDIES

William Harrison gingerly opens the padded box containing his
father John's timepiece, which has sailed with him all the way from
England. If it can be proved that this maritime chronometer —
which looks more like a giant fob watch than anything else — has
kept accurate time, despite the movement of the ship, the damp air
and changes in temperature, it will not only mean that, for the first
time in history, sailors will be able to chart their exact position at
sea with accuracy, but also that William's father John will be
eligible for a fortune in prize money! Any more than 2 minutes out,
and the prize is lost . . .

GRID LINES

If you look at a modern globe, you'll see that the Earth has
been divided up by a grid of lines. There are parallel lines,
running horizontally east to west. These are called lines of
latitude. Then there are lines running vertically from north
to south, *not* parallel, and all of them cutting through both
the North and South Poles. These are called lines of
longitude. The words 'latitude' and 'longitude' come from
the Latin *latus*, meaning wide, and *longus*, meaning length.

0° LATITUDE AND 0° LONGITUDE

The line of latitude running around the 'middle' of the
Earth (like a belt) is called the equator and is described as

0° latitude. Anywhere below the equator is described as being in the southern hemisphere. Anywhere above it is in the northern hemisphere. The middle line of longitude is called the prime meridian and is described as 0°. Dividing up maps with grid lines is a very, very, *very* old idea indeed, by the way. An ancient Greek named Eratosthenes was drawing maps with grid lines over 2,000 years ago!

MAP REFERENCES

To indicate a place on the globe you can give a map reference, stating the square in the grid where it will be found. To be even more accurate, each degree of latitude and longitude can be divided into 60 smaller units called minutes which, in turn, are divided into 60 seconds. (Each minute is one sea mile in length.) This way, anywhere in the world can be pinpointed. For example, the city of Edinburgh in Scotland can be found at 55° 55' N latitude, 3° 11' W longitude.

THE PROBLEM OF LONGITUDE

In the past, although most countries used lines of latitude and longitude on their maps, they didn't all agree which the prime meridian 0° line of longitude should be. They wanted it running through *their* particular country. (The matter was finally decided in 1884 when it was agreed that the line should run directly through Greenwich in London.) A far bigger problem was how to work out what your longitude was when you were at sea. Latitude could be worked out easily enough, using a special measuring instrument called a sextant, but longitude couldn't, which was a real problem for even the most experienced sailors. Half a map reference isn't much help when you're trying to plot your position out of sight of land!

A MATTER OF TIME

The Earth revolves a full 360° in 24 hours, which means that it must be revolving at a rate of 15° per hour. (I came up with that number simply by dividing 360 by 24.) For every 15° you travel east, the local time moves forward one hour, so every degree of longitude represents 4 minutes of time. If you know what time it is in Greenwich (at 0° longitude) and what time it is where you are, local time (from the position of the sun in the sky), then you can work out your longitude. How? By multiplying the difference between the times by 15 (because one hour equals 15°, remember). For example, if you're travelling east and it's 12:00 midday local time on board ship and still only 8:00 a.m. back in Greenwich, then the difference is 4 hours. Now, multiply that difference by 15° and you'll get your longitude: 60°. Cross-reference that with your easily worked-out degrees of latitude, and you'll know exactly where you are. Simple? Yes and no.

A MATTER OF TECHNOLOGY

It's only simple if you have an accurate watch or clock. Back in the seventeenth and eighteenth centuries, a few people had accurate pendulum clocks in their houses but these certainly wouldn't work on-board ship! One roll of the deck and the pendulum would be useless. Even if they could somehow keep the clock upright and the pendulum swinging steadily, changes in temperature and **humidity** – quite apart from the dangers of salt water – would make the clock go haywire! So surely no one would have considered such a solution because there was no such thing as a marine chronometer ('ship-proof' clock).

TOUCH AND GO

Without being able to calculate their longitude at sea, experienced sailors reached their destinations through sighting familiar landmarks along the way, and sticking to pre-plotted courses as best they could. At worst, ships went dangerously off course, smashing on rocks they weren't expecting to be there. Down the years thousands of lives and ships were lost because of it. In 1675, King Charles II of England founded the Royal Observatory at Greenwich to try to solve the pressing problem of being able to find your longitude when out at sea. It was hoped that the movement of the moon in the sky, in relation to easily spotted stars, could create a kind of lunar clock that could be used by sailors. Results were slow in coming.

DISASTER!

Finally, the British Admiralty had enough. In 1707, over 2,000 men died when four ships went off course when returning to England and ran aground on the Scilly Isles. The British Board of Longitude was set up to tackle the problem and, in 1714, they offered a £20,000 prize. The prize would be awarded to whoever devised a method of pinpointing a ship's longitude anywhere on Earth to within an accuracy of half a degree (2 minutes of time). The British weren't only interested in saving lives, though. They also knew that the country that discovered the secret of calculating longitude at sea could 'rule the waves', and this would affect all trade as well as military power.

A VARIETY OF SO-CALLED SOLUTIONS

Twenty thousand pounds in 1714 would be the equivalent of well over a million pounds today so, not surprisingly, a great many people were interested in the Longitude Board's prize. There were some very wacky ideas indeed, though the Board itself suspected that there would be an astrological solution – that somehow it would be possible to work out longitude by plotting the course of the moon and stars. Others worked on pseudoscientific, almost magical, solutions!

CRAZY AND CRUEL

One extraordinary suggestion was correctly based on the importance of knowing the time at $0°$ – but that was where the science ended and the craziness began. Here's what you had to do: first, injure a dog with a knife – sprinkled liberally with a special powder called the 'powder of sympathy' – then bandage the wound and take the dog on-board ship. Before you set sail, give an accomplice a set of the dog's bloody bandages. Once out at sea, part of your job is to make sure that the dog's wound never heals properly, and to listen out for the dog barking in pain on

the hour, every hour, the time it was back in Greenwich. And how will the dog know when the hour is reached back in Greenwich? Because of your accomplice, of course. He takes the bloody bandage and dunks it in a solution of water and some more of that 'powder of sympathy', thus magically linking it to the original wound and causing the dog to cry out on-board ship. Of course, *every* ship would need a wounded dog and an accomplice back on shore and, of course, it didn't work, but that's not to say that a number of countries didn't test out this fantastical approach!

A MATTER OF TIME

An Englishman named John Harrison (1693–1776), decided to stick with what he knew best: clocks. If one could design and build a clock that kept good time, even at sea, then the problem would be solved. It would, of course, have to be an extraordinary clock but, then again, Harrison was an extraordinary clockmaker. He even made some clocks

John Harrison, 1767

out of wood. Yes: wood. The cogs and everything. The first clock that Harrison was ready to test at sea was quite remarkable. Completed in 1735, it looked and worked like no other clock before it and caused much interest. In 1736, Harrison took it on his own sea trials to Lisbon and back (out aboard the *Centurion* and back aboard the *Orford*). He was pleased with the results but, perfectionist that he was, decided to build an even better clock.

IMPROVEMENTS TO BE MADE

Whilst Harrison worked on with funding from the Board, many Board members were hoping the solution lay elsewhere. What they were looking for was a clever naval solution involving charts of stars to guide them, preferably devised by a *gentleman*. They didn't want an amazingly simple mathematical solution based on an accurate 'marine chronometer' made by an uneducated clockmaker from the north! But Harrison didn't give up. In fact, he made it his life's work. He built version after version of his timepiece and was most pleased with the fourth: a much smaller, even more accurate clock, which looked like a giant fob watch. He finally completed it to his own satisfaction in 1759. In November 1761 it was carried aboard the *Deptford* by Harrison's son William, bound for Jamaica. The test of a trip to the West Indies was one of the original requirements of the competition. On arrival, William Harrison checked the watch. To be eligible for the prize, it mustn't be more than 2 minutes out (because this represented half a degree of longitude). As it turned out, it was less than 6 seconds slow!

A FINAL TEST

In a fair world, Harrison would probably have been awarded the prize there and then. As it was, the timepiece had to undergo *another* sea trial, aboard the *Tartar* bound for Barbados. Once again, Harrison's timepiece performed so well that it correctly predicted longitude to within half a degree. It worked! Harrison had discovered a way of accurately determining a ship's position, yet still the Board was reluctant to pay him!

RECOGNITION AT LAST

After appeals to King George III himself, it was finally the British parliament, not the Board of Longitude, that paid John Harrison his prize money in 1773. And it was richly deserved. The famous explorer Captain Cook took a timepiece, based on Harrison's design, on his second voyage of exploration. He declared it a complete success. This was proof enough that Harrison had discovered a way for ships to pinpoint their positions so accurately that

Captain James Cook on one of his many expeditions, 1774

they could avoid all charted dangers. The whole point of offering the prize had been to give the British Navy the advantage if a solution was found – whilst other countries had to rely on latitude and guesswork alone. As it was, sailors everywhere benefited from the new system. In fact, Harrison's method was used right up until recently by just about all navigators, until the advent of the Global Positioning System, where **satellites** can beam down a vessel's exact location on to a computer screen.

GERMS

6 JULY 1885, PARIS, FRANCE

Joseph Meister, a young boy, has been bitten fourteen times by a
dog suspected to have rabies – a frightening disease that can cause
foaming at the mouth, convulsions, paralysis and even death.
Joseph's mother pleads with the scientist Louis Pasteur to give her
son one of these vaccinations he's so famous for, but Pasteur has
never tried out a rabies vaccination on a human patient before.
Should he risk it? Has Joseph caught rabies from the bites?
If not, Pasteur might actually give him rabies when trying to
cure him. What should he do? He must decide. He must.
Time is running out . . .

WHAT YOU CAN'T SEE . . .

When something is so well known and somehow seems
so obvious, it's hard to imagine a time when people
didn't know it too. A really good example of this is germs.
It may seem hard to believe, but the existence of germs is

a relatively recent discovery. Less than 200 years ago, nobody knew about them. Hospitals didn't change sheets between patients, and surgeons used the same implements on different patients, one after the other, without cleaning them. And this applied to clothes too. A surgeon would proudly wear a grimy, blood-stained apron to show just how many operations he'd performed! It didn't occur to people that rivers full of rubbish didn't make the best drinking water, or how diseases actually spread.

FIGHTING SMALLPOX WITH SMALLPOX

About 300 years ago, the most feared disease of all was smallpox. Beginning with a high fever, back and muscle pain, and often vomiting, smallpox then covered the victim's body in pus-filled blisters (or sores) and usually killed you. If, however, you were lucky enough to live, then you couldn't catch it a second time ... though you may already have ended up scar-covered and blind. Doctors in Turkey noticed this and had a very clever idea. If they could deliberately give people a very mild form of smallpox, which the people would then recover from, then they might not get the disease again. But how to do it? They collected the fluid from the blisters of smallpox victims, scratched the arm of a healthy person and then rubbed the fluid into it.

SPREADING THE WORD

The wife of the British Ambassador to Turkey was Lady Mary Wortley Montagu. Afraid for her children's health during the smallpox outbreak, and impressed with the logic of what the doctors were trying, she had them treated this way. Lady Montagu was famous for her letter writing (collections of them were later published in books), and she took up the cause of encouraging British doctors back home to try inoculating people against smallpox in this way. None dared try it. The British doctors thought the risk of actually giving a perfectly healthy person a killer dose of smallpox was too high, but Lady Montagu had planted a seed of an idea in their minds.

A DISCOVERY AND AN IDEA

The big breakthrough came when British doctor Edward Jenner (1749–1823) made an important discovery. As well as smallpox, there was a much milder disease called cowpox. Also known as *vaccinia*, this was a disease humans could catch from cows. They were called 'poxes' because both diseases gave their victims fluid-filled blisters, but cowpox was very rarely fatal. In other words, victims of cowpox *lived*. What Jenner noticed was that people who'd had cowpox never

Edward Jenner, c 1800

seemed to get the deadly smallpox. The danger of the Turkish idea was that you could kill someone with that first dose of smallpox you were deliberately giving them. But what if you gave them a dose of the far-more-harmless *cow*pox instead? Might that have the same effect?

THE THEORY IS TESTED

In 1796, Edward Jenner found a milkmaid who'd caught cowpox from a cow. He took the fluid from one of the blisters on her hand and injected it into the arm of a perfectly healthy eight-year-old boy named James Phipps. James caught cowpox but wasn't seriously ill at all. Eight weeks later, Edward Jenner injected the boy again – this

time with the deadly smallpox fluid.
Fortunately for all concerned,
James was fine. Although it
was an extraordinarily risky
experiment to try out on
a child, Jenner had
discovered a way of
beating smallpox.

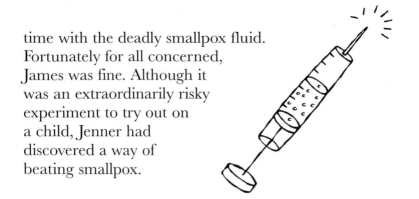

THAT'S HOW, BUT WHY?

Our bodies have an immune system, which fights to protect us against disease. When the cowpox was introduced into James Phipps's body, his immune system got to work at identifying what it was and finding a way of fighting it the best it could. (Sometimes our bodies fight a losing battle, when the disease wins and we die.) By the time that Jenner injected the smallpox, Phipps's immune system had 'learned' how to tackle poxes, and so destroyed it. At first, people ridiculed Edward Jenner and his findings, particularly because he didn't know what caused smallpox, simply how to prevent it. The whole idea sounded crazy, but it soon became obvious that people inoculated with cowpox were surviving outbreaks of smallpox, whilst others died.

A STUNNING RESULT

The smallpox vaccination, as it became known, was one of the most remarkable achievements in medical history. From being one of the most feared and deadly diseases across the whole world, it now no longer exists. After mass smallpox vaccination programmes across whole continents, it was declared in 1979 that there hadn't been a single reported case of smallpox anywhere in the world. Anywhere! The only existing smallpox **virus** existed not in victims but in scientific research laboratories. Sadly, one of the last people to die from smallpox was an English scientist.

THE BRILLIANT MONSIEUR PASTEUR

The word 'virus' was one adopted by Edward Jenner but 'vaccination' – named after cowpox, or *vaccinia* – wasn't. That was a term coined by Frenchman Louis Pasteur (1822–95), the man who really discovered germs and realized the role they played in diseases. Pasteur had already gained a reputation as a brilliant scientist when, in 1856, a Monsieur Bigo asked for his help. Monsieur Bigo's company made enormous amounts of

Louis Pasteur, c 1870

alcohol, in huge vats of fermenting beet juice and a variety of vegetables. The only trouble was, it kept going bad. Would Monsieur Pasteur look into the matter? Look into it he did, and the discovery he made and the conclusion he drew from it changed the world of medicine for ever.

THE MICRO WORLD OF MICROBES

Fermentation – the turning of fruit or vegetables into alcohol – was, in those days, thought to be a chemical reaction, where two or more substances interact together to produce a totally different product. When studied under a microscope, tiny, tiny blobs could be seen in the fermenting mixtures, but no real importance was attached to them. When Pasteur studied Monsieur Bigo's vats, however, he came to a startlingly different conclusion. He decided that these blobs were microbes: living things that could only be seen through a microscope. Furthermore, he decided that these particular microbes were yeasts (a kind of fungus, like toadstools and mushrooms). It was these yeast microbes, Pasteur argued, that turned the sugar into alcohol. Other scientists fell about laughing until he performed a number of tests to prove it. Fermentation without the yeast microbes just didn't happen. Fermentation with different types of microbes simply spoiled the mixture. So Pasteur had not only solved Monsieur Bigo's particular problem but had also led to the science of microbiology!

GERM ATTACK!

But Louis Pasteur took his discoveries one stage further. One of the main groups of microbes that he studied was bacteria. He found them living all over the place: in water, in the soil, in plants and even in people. Some of these microbes – some of these bacteria – Pasteur now suggested, were harmful, and he called these germs. Germs, he announced in a published work of 1858, caused illness and disease. One of the main arguments against this germ theory of disease was that the idea of these tiny living things somehow attacking and killing much larger living things (in other words you and me) seemed ridiculous! How could a tiny plant or creature, or whatever it was, invade a human body from the outside and win? The idea was preposterous. Preposterous or not, Pasteur had discovered the truth. It also went a long way to explaining why Jenner's vaccinations worked.

PASTEURIZATION

As Pasteur's reputation grew, he was asked by the Emperor of France, Napoleon III, to focus his attention on why so many French wines were turning sour. Pasteur quickly discovered that an invasion of the wrong types of microbe were the problem and, more importantly, that he could destroy them with heat. By heating wine (or beer) above 57 °C (135 °F) the germs would be killed but the taste and appearance unaffected. He then tried it on milk, which can contain many harmful bacteria, and it worked too. Today, in Britain, nearly all milk on sale is pasteurized (the name given to this process which, as you can see, was named after Pasteur). Again, here was another simple discovery that made all the difference.

germs killed by boiling

VACCINES

Over the years, Pasteur came to develop and understand many vaccines (which he named after the cowpox in recognition of Edward Jenner's earlier achievements), and he even found a vaccine against rabies. It could only be given once patients had been bitten but before they started showing any of the symptoms. When he tried it on badly bitten Joseph Meister in 1885, it saved the boy's life.

OTHER GREAT DISCOVERIES IN MEDICINE

In the fight against germs another great advance came in 1847. Many mothers and newborn babies suffered from 'childbed' or puerperal fever, which often spread from house to house. A Hungarian doctor called Ignaz Semmelweiss came up with the solution. He said that it might be a good idea if doctors present at childbirth *washed their hands* before and after delivering the baby! The reduction in the spread of the fever was dramatic. British surgeon Joseph Lister came up with an even more effective method of germ prevention. He had discovered that carbolic acid (usually a white crystal dissolved in water)

acted as a germ-killer, and he began using it in surgery. Lister had discovered antiseptic, another weapon in the fight against germs. The discovery of germs and how to defeat them has changed our world completely, saving millions upon millions of lives and transforming the levels of hygiene and quality of life across the globe. The discovery of anaesthetics and antibiotics were to have a startling effect too, as you can see in the next chapter.

ANAESTHETICS AND ANTIBIOTICS

1928, BACTERIOLOGY LAB, ST MARY'S HOSPITAL, LONDON

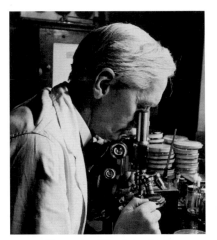

Alexander Fleming, 1943

Alexander Fleming's laboratory is as cluttered as always. Every worktop is covered with something, and the sink in the laboratory is piled high with petri dishes. Each petri dish – small, round and with a tightly fitting lid – contains bacteria, used as part of Fleming's experiments on flu germs. Back from his summer holiday, Fleming is opening each petri dish in turn, looking at the bacteria and then soaking it in cleaning solution, until . . . he notices one of the petri dishes has something furry growing in it – some kind of mould. These things happen. The lid can't have been on properly. Tests sometimes get contaminated and spoiled. Then Fleming looks closer, with a mixture of scientific interest and mounting excitement. There's no bacteria around the edge of the mould, it's all to the side. Could this mysterious mould have somehow killed these germs? And what exactly is it?

mysterious mould

TAKE AWAY THE PAIN

As well as those remarkable discoveries in the previous chapter, there have been many other advances in medicine, probably none more important than antibiotics: the drugs that can tackle all sorts of different germs. But, before their discovery, came another milestone in medical treatment: anaesthetics. Anaesthetics help to deaden pain – either by putting the patient to sleep (a general anaesthetic) or by numbing the area to be operated on (a local anaesthetic). Before their discovery and use, patients would usually be wide awake when their legs were amputated or their bodies cut open. Patients were often soldiers or sailors injured in fighting, and they might be lucky enough to have had a smoke of hemp (which is a plant also used for making ropes) or a swig of rum to relax

An operation in 1895

73

them – but it would still have been agony, and they would have to have been held down on the table. Early general anaesthetics included laughing gas and a liquid called ether. The trouble with ether was that it was difficult to know how much to give to the patient for it to be effective. Patients often woke up halfway through being operated on, or were very sick afterwards. In 1831, an American chemist called Samuel Guthrie created a drug called chloroform but it wasn't used in an operation for sixteen years.

A ROYAL THUMBS-UP

Scottish surgeon James Simpson was eager to find a way to make operations less painful and frightening for his patients, but he wasn't happy with ether. He knew about the waking-up-early and being-violently-sick **side effects** so, in 1847, he thought he should try this chloroform he'd heard about. But who should he try it out on? In the end, he decided to take the chloroform himself, along with two other doctors (Dr Duncan and Dr Keith). This they did – and all immediately collapsed to the floor asleep. Though sleeping, Dr Keith kept kicking the bottom of a table with his feet, and waving his arms about. The other two doctors lay as still as two sacks of potatoes. When they finally woke up, Simpson declared his rather unusual experiment a complete success! It wasn't until Queen Victoria was given

chloroform in 1853 when giving birth to her eighth child – she had nine altogether, and the eighth one was Leopold – that it suddenly caught on and became all the rage.

X-RAYS

Another remarkable discovery for the medical profession was the X-ray. Discovered accidentally in 1895 by the German physicist Wilhelm Roentgen, X-rays can take photographs of the inside of a person's body: bones and inner organs. This way, many problems can be revealed without the doctor having to cut the patient open. One of the problems with actually operating on a patient, you see, is the added risk of infection. An operation might cure them of one thing, and promptly kill them with germs! This is why one of the greatest lifesavers of all was the discovery of antibiotics – drugs that can kill all sorts of different types of germs rather than just one particular type.

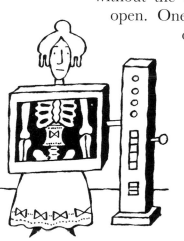

ALEXANDER FLEMING

In 1922, Alexander Fleming discovered a natural antiseptic in tears, but he is best remembered for his discovery of the first known antibiotic: penicillin. The importance of this discovery becomes clear when you realize that penicillin could even have prevented the bubonic plague epidemics in

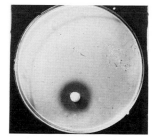

Penicillin growing in a petri dish, 1943

the Middle Ages, which killed millions of people! When Fleming discovered penicillin – for that was the mysterious mould he discovered on the petri dish at the start of this chapter – it didn't cause much excitement or interest when he published his findings. Fleming himself worked on the mould, but growing it in reasonable amounts proved very difficult. So here was a potentially lifesaving wonder drug that was largely being ignored.

FLOREY AND CHAIN

All that was about to change, thanks to pathologist Howard Walter Florey. Florey was born in Australia but came to England to study and, later, to teach. After being made director of the Dunn School of Pathology, part of Oxford University, in 1935, he began studies on Fleming's penicillin mould. By 1939, he and Ernst Boris Chain – a Jewish German who'd left Berlin following the rise of Nazism – had not only found which part of the mould was the active, germ-killing ingredient, but had also worked out ways of producing more of the drug. Then came the Second World War. With all British resources being turned to the war effort, and with the British government having no idea just how important penicillin would prove to be, Florey went to the USA.

TAKING PENICILLIN

One of the problems with penicillin in its original form was that you couldn't simply swallow it: all its 'healing' powers were destroyed by digestive juices before it could have any effect. You couldn't be given penicillin in an injection either because, at this stage, it contained too many other impurities that might do you more harm than good. Florey and Chain managed to produce pure penicillin, but in very small amounts. In early tests on a patient, penicillin was in such short supply that it had to be chemically extracted from the patient's urine and used again! In the USA, enough penicillin was eventually produced to help the fight against germs infecting wounded soldiers, and its true worth was proved. Even then, it was cheaper and easier to make the drug from enormous vats of fermenting mould than to produce it chemically in a laboratory. Today, however, it can be mass-produced chemically, both cheaply and effectively.

HIGHEST HONOURS

The war ended in 1945, the same year that Alexander Fleming, Howard Walter Florey and Ernst Chain were jointly awarded the Nobel Prize for Medicine – Fleming, for realizing the importance, if not the possibilities, of his accidental discovery, and Florey and Chain for turning these possibilities into a lifesaving reality. A variety of antibiotics has been widely available since the 1950s and

what were once considered life-threatening diseases are now treatable. Pneumonia and TB (tuberculosis), which used to be the deadliest of diseases, can now be cured. And more and more complicated operations can be carried out thanks to antibiotics too, now that there's less chance of those dreaded infections. In the past, many simple operations were surgically successful – what needed putting right was put right – but then the patient died from infection. Not so today. Antibiotics have changed the world of medicine almost beyond recognition.

GENETICS

8 MARCH 1865, BRÜNN SOCIETY FOR THE STUDY OF NATURAL SCIENCE

Gregor Mendel stands before the assembled audience. The paper he has just read contains information that could completely alter the understanding of biology as we know it. His research, discoveries and conclusions could rock the very foundations of existing beliefs on human life itself – if only someone was interested. The guests had come here expecting to hear a talk on plants; instead, he's given them a talk on genetics and they just don't understand what he's told them. Have all his years of painstaking hard work really gone to waste?

Gregor Johann Mendel (1822–84) was a man whose brilliance was never recognized in his own lifetime but whose discoveries were later – *much* later – taken up by others; without a doubt, they changed the world. Mendel was an Austrian born to a poor peasant family in what is now the Czech Republic. He later became a monk in an Augustinian monastery at Brünn (also now in the Czech Republic) which, even then, had a reputation for being a place of scientific learning. After studying at the University of Vienna, he failed to get a teaching degree and returned to the monastery as an abbot. There, he began his years of careful experimentation.

PEAS, GLORIOUS PEAS

Between 1856 and 1863, Mendel grew and cross-bred over 28,000 pea plants of different varieties. He studied

everything from the heights of the various plants to the shape of the pods and the peas within them and the colours of their flowers. Then he bred tall plants with short plants, smooth pea plants with knobbly pea plants, white-flowered plants with purple-flowered plants, straight podded plants with bent podded plants. You name it, he tried it. He then studied the **offspring** pea plants this cross-breeding created and made some very important discoveries.

TALL PLANT, SHORT PLANT

Using the heights of the plants as an example – either tall or short – here's what he discovered. If tall plants were only bred with other tall plants, you only ever got tall plants. And breeding short plants with short plants (pure-breeding) always resulted in short plants. If you cross-bred pure-bred tall plants with pure-bred short plants, however, you always ended up with tall offspring too – *never* short ones. Next, Mendel cross-bred these new offspring (with one tall and one short parent) and made an interesting discovery. Although the new parents were all tall, for every three tall offspring they had, they had one short one. (This is called a ratio of 3 to 1, or 3:1). Mendel worked out why.

A PAIR OF GENES

He suggested that each parent plant had a pair of (what we now call) genes. For example, a pure-bred tall plant had two 'tall' height genes (which we'll show as TT) and a pure-bred small plant had two 'small' height genes (which we'll show as SS). But, he went on, each parent must only give *one* gene from the pair to their offspring (one T or one S). This meant that the offspring of TT (tall) and SS (short) parents would always end up with one of four combinations of the TS genes. Because all the offspring turned out tall, T must be a stronger, more dominant gene than small's S. Mendel called this 'dominance'. When these TS offspring had offspring of their own, though, why was every fourth plant small, Mendel wondered? Because the height genes of two TS parent plants combining leave you with TT TS ST SS – and where there's no dominant tall T height gene and just two small SS height genes, the plant has no other other option than to be small!

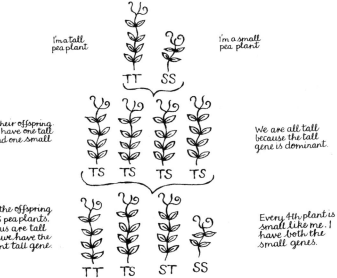

I'm a tall pea plant

TT   SS

I'm a small pea plant

We are their offspring. We each have one tall gene and one small gene.

TS   TS   TS   TS

We are all tall because the tall gene is dominant.

We are the offspring of the TS pea plants. Three of us are tall because we have the dominant tall gene.

TT   TS   ST   SS

Every 4th plant is small like me. I have both the small genes.

REGRESSIVENESS

What was so important about this was that although the offspring of the cross-bred pure-bred tall and pure-bred small plants all appeared to be tall, they all had the short, less dominant height gene in them, which did nothing *until they too had offspring.* This gene would then be able to reappear in every fourth offspring (which Mendel called 'regressing', in other words 'going back to being' as short as one of its grandparents). So Mendel had not only discovered that the parents had pairs of genes for different functions, and only gave one from each pair to their offspring, but he also discovered dominant and regressive genes – and this doesn't just apply to plants and animals but to you and me too, with everything from eyes to hair colour!

TOO CLEVER BY HALF

Mendel's Laws are still the basis for genetic research today, but in 1866 Mendel was so far ahead of his time that no one seemed to understand his ideas, let alone take any notice of his published results or talks. Part of the problem was that he explained his ideas with numbers and statistics, rather than as simply as possible. In 1900, a number of people picked up on his discoveries and began to realize their importance, but it wasn't until even later that their full significance was discovered.

DNA

We now know that the nucleus of every human cell contains a DNA **molecule**. 'DNA' is short for 'deoxyribonucleic acid'. *Very* short for 'deoxyribonucleic acid', which is why everyone, including scientists, usually refers to it as 'DNA'. DNA contains the genes, or instructions, that pass on characteristics from one generation of a family to the next, in the same way that Mendel's peas did. As long ago as 1869, scientists realized that there was DNA in our cells, but they weren't very sure what it did, or what the molecule actually looked like.

A representation of human DNA

THE BUILDING BLOCKS OF LIFE

By the 1950s, scientists had reached the startling conclusion that DNA was a very complicated molecule made up of much simpler ones, which can be imagined as the 'building blocks of life'. Put the blocks together in a different order and you get a different form of life, because all living things – plants or animals – contain DNA. The only problem was that scientists didn't actually yet know the structure of DNA or how it reproduced itself, to pass on to the next generation.

DISCOVERING THE DOUBLE HELIX

James Watson with the original DNA model, 1994

The two people responsible for calculating that the DNA molecule is a double helix in shape – once described to me as being a bit like a rope ladder being twisted into a spiral – were the British scientist Francis Crick and the American scientist James Watson, in 1953. Although they were the ones who made this public breakthrough, they did it based on scientific data from two other British scientists: the physicist Maurice Wilkins and crystallographer Rosalind Franklin. Rosalind Franklin's data, including a photograph she had managed to take of a DNA molecule, the only one in existence, was shown to Crick and Watson without her knowledge. Sadly, she did not receive the Nobel Prize with Crick, Watson and Wilkins. She had died of cancer by the time they were given this great honour.

GENETIC ENGINEERING

Once DNA had been understood in this way, many scientists wanted to see what would happen if they moved around these 'building blocks of life'. This process is called genetic engineering: altering nature – whether plants or animals – to, supposedly, help humankind. This was first achieved at a very basic level in 1973 in the USA.

DOLLY THE CLONE

Today, genetic engineering is very rarely out of the news. Cloning has also become a reality. Once the stuff of science fiction, it is now possible to create one living, breathing animal from the cell of another, without the need for 'parents'. The first example of this was Dolly the sheep, first revealed to the world in 1997. Dolly, named after the country singer Dolly Parton, was cloned from the single cell of an adult sheep by Dr Ian Wilmut in Scotland. Many fear that human cloning will one day take place. Some people believe that this would be morally and ethically wrong.

FRANKENSTEIN FOODS

Another area of genetics causing a great deal of controversy is genetically modified crops and food. Some scientists believe that, by subtly changing the genetic make-up of some foods, they can be made bigger, or more **nutritious**, or more resistant to disease, for example. Such altered crops are called genetically modified or GM crops. Many people who are opposed to scientists supposedly 'tampering with nature' call them 'Frankenstein food' after the

likes wet conditions

character of Dr Frankenstein, who created a monster. These people are concerned that genetically modified crops could upset the ecosystem and the environment.

flies off the tree

DNA FINGERPRINTING

In the 1980s, another important and completely different use for DNA was discovered: people can be 'genetically fingerprinted'. Everyone's fingerprints are unique and, if left at a crime scene, can be matched against a suspect's prints taken at the police station. Genetic 'fingerprints' aren't really fingerprints at all, but they can help match up a suspect with a crime. For example, the saliva on an apple found at a crime scene can be checked for DNA and compared against another DNA sample taken from a suspect. Today, DNA samples taken from 3,000 year-old Egyptian mummies are being used to work out the family relationships between the dead pharaohs, queens, princes and princesses who ruled that ancient civilization!

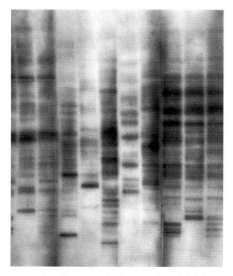

The first genetic fingerprint, 1984

WHAT NEXT?

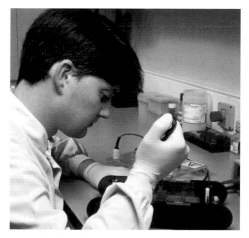

A scientist beginning the process of separating DNA fragments

Some people view the future of genetic engineering with great excitement, believing that it might be possible to clone human organs so that diseased or destroyed organs – such as hearts and livers, for example – can be replaced without the need for donors. Others fear that it may lead to 'eugenics'

– the careful manipulation of genes to create 'perfect' people, with the sex that you want, the size that you want, the hair and colour of eyes that you want – rather than letting nature take its course. The discovery of DNA and genetics has certainly opened up whole new horizons – and a can of worms!

PLASTICS

1907, HUDSON RIVER VALLEY, NEW YORK STATE, USA

The son of a Belgian shoemaker, American chemist Leo Hendrik Baekeland has already made his fortune selling his photographic paper, Velox, to George Eastman of Kodak for $750,000 in 1899. Now he is hard at work on a new challenge in his laboratory, the converted stable block of his home, Snug Rock. Baekeland has spent five years trying to produce a plastic, using substances extracted from coal tar and wood alcohol, and for year after year all he's come up with is a useless mass of goo. Until now! At last, at long last, he's produced a resin that doesn't burn, melt or dissolve once hardened into shape. He's developed the world's first practical synthetic plastic!

A RECENT DISCOVERY

Today, so many things are made of colourful, lightweight, tough, easily moulded plastics that it's quite hard to imagine – or, if you're older, to *remember* – life without them. It's not that long ago that people listened to music on records, not CDs, and what were those earliest records

(called 78s) made from? Plastic? Wrong. They were made from beetle secretions. Yup, you read that right. Records used to be made of a kind of resin squeezed out of

89

lac beetles, called shellac. (It's said to have taken 15,000 beetles six months to produce just 453 grams or 1 lb, so you can imagine how expensive it was!) Fortunately for us, and for the beetles, the discovery of **synthetic** plastics has changed all that. Today, everything from light switches to artificial hips is made of plastic!

EASY TO USE

Plastics are light, hard-wearing and easy to clean, but also tough, waterproof and cheap to make. They don't rust or rot either – which can be a good thing and a bad thing – and they can easily be made into just about any shape. Plastic is a name given to materials that have giant, organic molecules – I'll explain more about that later, have no fear – that can be formed into just about any shape we want, using a variety of different methods.

EYES ON THE PRIZE

In 1860, a firm that made ivory billiard and pool balls in the USA offered a $10,000 prize for anyone who could come up with a substitute for the ivory. Inventor John Wesley Hyatt discovered a way of producing a transparent, colourless plastic, which could be easily dyed and moulded. This was the very first plastic and Hyatt called it celluloid. He didn't win the prize, but he did have great success with celluloid. It had two drawbacks, though. First, a British inventor claimed that he'd already come up with the same plastic but had called it xylonite. Secondly, celluloid was highly flammable: it caught fire very easily and, when it

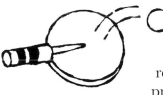

burned, it *really* burned! One of its main uses was for camera film. Today, a more fire-resistant version of celluloid is probably most commonly used for ping-pong balls.

THE BAKELITE BREAKTHROUGH

An early Bakelite radio

Then Baekeland discovered how to produce the first **thermosetting plastic** – Bakelite – in about 1907, and soon everything from wirelesses – what we'd now call radios and which, up until then, had been in wooden cases – to cameras, pens and telephones was being made from it. Plastic is a good **insulator** so is ideal for casing electrical products. Rather than bright colours, Bakelite was usually black, brown or tortoiseshell and was very brittle. It cracked easily if knocked too hard. Baekeland became fabulously rich and sold his company and retired to Florida in 1939. Finding the climate hot, he used to enjoy standing fully clothed in his swimming pool!

BUILDING THOSE CHAINS

The 1920s and 1930s saw major discoveries and breakthroughs in the understanding of plastics – that small molecules (often referred to as monomers) can be linked together to create long-chain molecules and that these long-chain molecules can be linked to other long-chain molecules to create really, *really* big molecules of stretchy, mouldable plastics. Molecules made of linked-up monomers are called polymers, from the Greek word 'poly', meaning 'many bits'.

DIFFERENT PLASTICS, DIFFERENT USES

One of the great things about plastics is that scientists soon discovered that, by mixing and matching different monomers to make different polymers, they could create different types of plastics for different uses. For example, some plastics soften and melt when they're heated because their polymers – long-chain molecules – are side-by-side rather than all linked together. These are called thermoplastics. Other types of plastics, called thermosetting plastics, don't melt because their polymers are tightly linked.

POLYTHENE, PVC and POLYPROPYLENE

A good example of two very common and different types of plastic are polythene and PVC. Polythene can be made as thin as paper and is ideal for using as a transparent film to wrap food in. PVC, on the other hand, is much tougher

A dial telephone, 1929   *A Bush television, c 1950*

and can be used to make everything from trousers to luggage. Polythene was developed by the German scientist Karl Zieglar in 1953. He shared the Nobel Prize for Chemistry with Giulo Natta (the developer of polypropylene) in 1963 for their work on polymers and plastics. Polypropylene is a thermoplastic which is ideal for making anything from bottles to brush bristles to carpets.

THE RAW MATERIALS

The earliest plastics were made from substances discovered in milk, coal, cotton and even wood.

Today, the most important basic ingredients for plastics come from oil. The oil that comes up out of the ground when drilled – the thick, black gooey liquid – is called crude oil. This is then heated up in a fractionating (separating) tower in an oil refinery. The heat causes the crude oil to separate into different types of liquid which are, in turn, used to create different products. These are mainly

fuels: petrol, diesel oil and paraffin, but also a liquid called naphtha. It is this naphtha that is used in the plastics process. It is reheated to create a substance called ethylene, from which millions of polyethylene chips (plastic pellets) are produced.

SHAPING PLASTICS

Plastics can be shaped into objects in a variety of different ways. The most obvious is moulding, where hot, liquid plastic is poured into a mould and air is blown into the mould (pressing the plastic to the sides). Then, when the plastic has cooled down and become hard, the mould is opened and the plastic removed. It's taken on the shape of the mould but is hollow inside – ideal for everything from bottles to footballs. Another method, extrusion, is when hot, melted plastic is forced through a hole of the desired shape and size, which when cool and hard makes long hollow tubes – for pipes, guttering, etc. By blowing gas bubbles into melted plastic, hard or soft foam plastics can be made. One of the most common plastic foams is polystyrene, often used to make fast-food containers.

PLASTIC CLOTHES

If all you think of are plastic macs and PVC jackets and trousers when you think of plastic clothes, think again. Plastics can actually be made into long, thin threads and woven into garments. To make the plastic threads, melted plastic is forced through tiny holes in a machine – a bit like the rose on the end of a watering can – called a spinneret.

Whilst still warm, these threads can be stretched even further and thinner. The first and most famous of these plastic threads is nylon, which came about as the result of research and experiments by one Wallace Carothers.

WALLACE CAROTHERS

American scientist Wallace Carothers (1896–1937) was such a brilliant chemistry student that his college asked him to become a teacher! He later went on to become a teacher at Harvard, the most prestigious university in the USA, but was persuaded to leave and join the DuPont company in 1928 as head of research in organic chemistry. It was at DuPont that Carothers and his team of eight worked on long-chain polymers in a special lab set up to study 'pure science'. They nicknamed the building Purity Hall.

A BIT OF LUCK

It was in Purity Hall that, one day in 1930, a member of Carothers's team – Julian Hill – looked into a vat containing one of Carothers's polymer resins and dipped a glass rod in it, to give it a prod. Pulling the rod out, he found the resin stuck to the end of it and, as he walked backwards across the room, he was amazed to find that it stretched out into a long plastic thread! When news got out that Carothers's team were on their way to developing a human-made plastic that could be woven into clothes, there was much excitement. The problem was, if washed or ironed, the new fibre melted into a horrible gooey mess. More work certainly needed to be done!

NYLON

The breakthrough came in 1934 when Carothers developed a new approach for synthesizing these giant polymers, resulting in a strong plastic fibre that didn't melt below 195° C. It originally appeared on the market as toothbrush bristles under the name of Exton! In 1938, DuPont finally announced that their laboratories had produced 'the first man-made organic textile fabric prepared entirely from new materials from the mineral kingdom'. They called it 'nylon' and nylon stockings first went on sale in 1940. They were a huge success. Sadly, Carothers didn't live to see this. Less than three weeks after DuPont filed for a **patent** on nylon, he killed himself by drinking the poison cyanide. Despite his incredible discoveries and achievements, Carothers often felt depressed and a failure. He'd had a breakdown and even spent time in asanatorium. In his short life, however, he certainly left a lasting legacy.

Steam treating nylon stockings, 1946

PLUSES AND MINUSES

You only have to sit inside a modern car to see how plastics dominate the lives of so many of us today. The steering wheel, gear knob, dashboard, door handles, head rests, even the paint – in fact, just about *everything* you see – contains plastics. But, despite their many excellent uses, you only have to look on a rubbish tip to see the problems plastics cause the world too. Unlike natural substances, such as paper or wood, they decompose very slowly (if at all). Very few plastics are biodegradable (in other words, they're not broken down by bacteria when buried). So plastics have done much to pollute our world too. The solution probably lies in recycling: collecting old, unwanted plastic items to be cleaned, sorted and melted down to make new ones or, better still, reusing items such as plastic bags rather than throwing them away the first time. Plastics are like so many of the other discoveries in this book. It's what people do with them that makes such a difference – good or bad – to our planet.

GLOSSARY

air resistance – the force of the air resisting and slowing a falling object

amp – a unit of electricity (as in a 13-amp plug) used for measuring the amount of current required to produce a certain amount of force between two wires. Named after André Ampère

battery – a device that converts chemical energy into electrical energy, by means of a chemical reaction that produces a flow of electrons

c – short for the Latin word 'circa', meaning 'about'. A date marked c means an approximate date; the event occurred around about then

colonists – people setting up and living in a colony

colour blind – the inability to distinguish certain colours

compound – a substance that contains atoms of two or more elements

conductor – material through which electricity flows freely

conquistadors – sixteenth-century Spanish conquerors of the Americas

constitution – the stated rights of the people and the powers of their government

element – a substance that cannot be split into simpler substances

farad – a unit of electrical capacity named after Faraday

heresy – beliefs or statement going against the official rulings of the Church

humidity – warmth and dampness

in theory – believed, but untried and untested

independently – on your own, without help from others

insulator – something which, in the case of an electrical insulator, stops electricity passing through it

intercontinental ballistic missile – a missile with a nuclear warhead that can travel over 5,500 km

low church – Christians who were against statues and finery, believing in humility (being humble) and simplicity

low-resistance an easy route for electricity, down a high conductor (resistance is the opposition of flow to an electric current)

mass – the amount of physical matter an object contains, nowadays usually measured in grams

misconception – a commonly held belief that isn't actually true

molecule – usually two or more atoms bonded together

Nazism – beliefs of the Nazi party (led by Adolf Hitler)

Nobel Prize – an annual prize given for outstanding contributions to physics, chemistry, physiology, medicine, literature, peace, and now economics too. Awarded by an international committee in Sweden (except for the peace prize, awarded in Norway)

nuclear fallout – side effects, secondary consequences of nuclear explosion

nucleus *plural:* **nuclei** – the heart of an atom, made up of protons and neutrons

nutritious – full of nutrients, which your body can use to keep you strong and healthy

offspring – a plant's, animal's or human's 'child'

patent – a legal permit designed to stop others stealing your invention. A patent prevents everyone else from making or selling the invention you have patented

patron – a benefactor or someone who sponsors another to do some work, e.g. research, painting

phenomena *single:* **phenomenon** – occurrences

sap – the liquid in trees and plants. Tree sap often hardens into a goo

satellite – a machine orbiting the Earth (often receiving signals from and sending signals to satellite dishes on Earth)

side effects – effects in addition to those actually intended (for example, side effects of loud music might be a headache or ringing in the ears)

sovereign – a king or queen

Soviet – someone from the Soviet Union, a communist federal republic in Eastern Europe and North Asia led by Russia and known as the USSR. Disbanded in 1991

spectrum – the full range of colours making up white light: red, orange, yellow, blue, green, indigo, violet

subatomic – smaller than an atom. Subatomic particles include electrons, protons and neutrons

synthetic – human-made or artificial

thermosetting plastic – type of plastic that doesn't melt when heated

vacuum – a place without gas or air, as in space

virus – an organism that multiplies in the body's cells, often causing disease

volt – a unit for measuring the electrical potential between two points – the work that has to be done to move a unit of positive charge from one point to another. Named after Alessandro Volta

watt – a unit of electrical power (as in 60-watt light bulb)

PHILIP ARDAGH

Imagine the unimaginable: a world without computers, cars, telephones or aeroplanes. Have you ever wondered how such things were invented?

From early steam trains to underground tube trains, from parachutes to Concorde, this book is bursting with facts, figures and amazing photographs that look at the evolution of inventions that have made the world what it is today.

Eureka!